Wild Flowers as They Grow

BUTTERBUR

Wild Flowers as They Grow

Photographed in Colour
Direct from Nature by

H. Essenhigh Corke

F.R.P.S., F.R.H.S.

With Descriptive Text by

G. Clarke Nuttall

B.Sc.

Fifth Series

CASSELL AND COMPANY, LTD
LONDON, NEW YORK, TORONTO AND MELBOURNE
1913

CONTENTS

36635

vi Contents

LIST OF PLATES

List of Plates

WILD FLOWERS AS THEY GROW

THE BUTTERBUR

PETASITES VULGARIS

THE wind blew chill in the March days over the boggy meadow. A little stream made its way sluggishly through the swampiness. Though

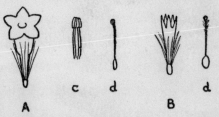

A, male floret. *c*, stamens (5), anthers joined. *d*, rudimentary ovary, style, stigma. B, female floret. *d*, stigma, style, ovary.

in the spinney adjacent some of the trees were flowering after their rather sad and subdued fashion, there was, as yet, little hint of spring gaiety to be seen around. Later the meadow would be a garden

101

of beautiful flowers, but not yet, for the spring was still in its infancy. On the wet earth by the brookside, however, remarkable cone-like structures of a pinkish flesh colour were rising—" Boghorns " the country folk aptly term them—which gave a touch of warmth to the lush greenness, but which in their hue, bareness, and general unlikeness to ordinary flowers almost suggested some big fungus. It was the Butterbur, one of the earliest of spring flowers, a plant that haunts wet ditches and brooksides, but which, in spite of its frequency in Britain, is yet curiously unfamiliar to the generality of people. Perhaps its colour, so like the sandy soil that it prefers, shields it a little from observation, perhaps the fact that it grows in very damp quarters that one avoids at that season makes it less known.

After the fashion of its near relative, the coltsfoot, it also divides the cycle of its life into two very distinct episodes, and, "putting the cart before the horse," as we are apt to say, produces its flowers before its leaves. Its creeping, underground

The Butterbur

stem provides, not merely one kind of shoot, but two, namely, leafless flower-shoots and flowerless leaf-shoots, and the flower-shoots awake and finish their day in the spring before the summer calls the leaf-shoots into maturity. In the " Boghorns," then, we have episode number one. A very fine specimen of a " Boghorn" may be as much as a foot high, but as a rule the growth is nearer half this measurement. Each has a thick, fleshy, erect axis, and along this arise on very short stalks a number of cup-shaped heads of flowers, the cup being but slightly hollowed out. There may be fifty or more of these flower-heads on each, and each head may itself consist of some fifty florets. Below the flower-clusters a few colourless bracts cling to the axis.

Now, though, perhaps, a keen observer would notice that some of the axes were shorter and rather more loosely set with flower-heads than others, and, moreover, that these same flower-heads were somewhat small in comparison with those in the denser

Wild Flowers as They Grow

cones, still the superficial divergences are hardly such as to suggest fundamental differences in nature. Yet the Butterbur is known to botanists as a diœcious plant; that is, it has its male flowers all on one plant, its female flowers all on another, and here the looser, shorter clusters of smaller heads represent the male element, and the larger heads and denser, longer spikes represent the female. Occasionally there is a slight interchange between the sexes, and a few female flowers mingle with the males, and a few males with the females, but not as a rule. The florets individually are very small and a good hand lens is necessary if one would accurately make out their structure.

The male florets individually consist of a calyx represented by a few scanty hairs; a pink corolla as a small tube below, but expanding into a bell-shape with five lobes; magenta-headed stamens—five— their anthers all joined in a ring; and a seedless ovary with a style, but minus the stigmas necessary for the reception of pollen to complete its struc-

The Butterbur

ture. Abundant honey lies in the petal tube. The course of events is the same as in many other members of the *Compositæ* family—the anthers burst inwards and the pollen is swept out of their ring by the growth of the style, and lies in a mass on top.

The female florets are not supplied with honey, neither have they any stamens, not even useless remains of any; their corolla is merely a thread-like tube, which contains the style, furnished in this case with the necessary stigma, while the calyx is formed of numerous hairs. In both florets the ovary is outside and below the petals. It is stated that, as a rule, the Butterbur is fertilised by small flies and creeping insects to whom its flesh-like hue particularly appeals; moreover, its low and unprotected situation on the ground obviously encourages their perambulations over its surface. But the Butterbur in the boggy meadow with which we started was alive with bees on that sunny, if cold, March morning, and they flew from head to head with manifest eagerness, thus bridging the gap between male and female colonies.

Each female floret produces a single seed which carries the calyx crown or "pappus" of white hairs, so that it is easily caught and carried by the wind.

While the flowers are going through their career a few small leaves may occasionally push up by their side, but it is not till the flowering is over that the Butterbur really enters upon the second and no less remarkable stage in its life cycle. "Lagwort" it is sometimes called for this reason, but once the leaf-shoots make a start they grow with tropical luxuriance and the great leaves, one to each main stem, may become even a yard in diameter, their smooth, dark green, delicate tissue stretching unbroken from rib to rib. The stalk is at one side, with the blade of the leaf almost at right angles to it; and, hence, the ribs that uphold the blade, radiating from the point of attachment of the blade on the girder principle, must needs be thick, strong and prominent. To these enormous leaves the

The Butterbur

plant owes several of its synonyms. Thus it is
" Bog Rhubarb," " Poison Rhubarb," and " Umbrella Plant," also " Flapperdock," and its corruption " Blatterdock." They also account for its
generic name *Petasites*—*petasos* being the Greek
word for the felt hats worn by shepherds and
agriculturists—because they are large enough to
form hats. The broad cap of Mercury is this same
petasos. The English country equivalent is " Capdockin," a name sometimes heard. No other vegetation can live where these leaves grow ; they exclude light and air to a fatal extent from all
beneath. Indeed, in themselves they are, as has
been pointed out, " our most remarkable example
of those (leaves) adapted to situations in which
the supply of water is considerable, the air moist,
and the light not too strong."

The root of the Butterbur probably plays a
greater part than the feather-crowned seeds in propagating the plant, for it is the most vigorous of
creepers. One observer relates that a little piece

Wild Flowers as They Grow

of root, two inches long and the thickness of one's finger, was planted, and after only eighteen months was examined, when it was found that it had formed many shoots six feet long which had penetrated to a depth of two feet, while from a mere nothing its weight had become eight pounds. It has a black skin, and is full of a resinous and bitter juice.

A common name of the plant, " Pestilence Wort," recalls the fact that in the evil days of the plague the herbalists prescribed it as a specific, for " Butterburre dried and made into powder and then dronken is a souveraine medicine against the Plague and Pestilent fevers, because it provoketh sweate and for that cause it driveth from the harte all venim and evill heate." Less than a hundred years ago it was stated that during an epidemic of a peculiarly virulent fever, the English died wholesale because they bled themselves, while the Germans recovered and lived by making use of Butterbur. They sliced the roots and added boiling water ; when cold they poured off the liquor and put into it sugar and

The Butterbur

mountain wine, and then drank a quarter of a pint every fourth hour, with the result, we are told, that their spirits were raised, their anguish and depression passed, and they speedily recovered health. After a further eulogy the writer of " The Universal Herball," concludes, " I could say much on this subject, but it would be an unnecessary task to prove the sun gives light ; and it is no less certain that this root is the best known remedy for putrid and pestilential fevers." And yet to-day it does not even find mention in our pharmacopœia !

As for the name Butterbur, several centuries ago it was suggested that it arose because housewives wrapped their butter in it in hot weather. Dr. Pryor, however, thinks that it is due to a confusion of the French *bourre*, whence " bur " in burdock, with the French *beurre*—butter, but when we recall how often butter and cream cheese are to-day wrapped in the very similar rhubarb leaf, the earlier and simpler explanation will probably be better accepted.

THE LESSER PERIWINKLE

VINCA MINOR

"THE Periwinkle is a great binder," said an old herbalist, and its name implies as much for Periwinkle is a corruption of the M. Latin *pervincula*, derived from *per* = about, and *vincere* =

a, calyx. *b*, petals. *c d*, stamens, stigma, with hairy brush-style. *c*, stamens (side and front view). *d*, hairs, plate-like stigma, style; ovary with two nectaries.

to bind. It is a " binder " in many senses, too. In the first place literally, for its strong, supple shoots are used at times as cords; in the second place, they are twined into garlands to bind round

The Lesser Periwinkle

the brows of the youthful dead—particularly in Italy—the evergreen leaves being a symbol of immortality ; once, too, they formed garlands of derision, as, for instance, when Simon Fraser, that loyal adherent of Wallace, was taken in irons through London with " a garland of Pervenke set on his heved ; " thirdly, it was a " binder " in medicine, for if its leaves were chewed, said the herbalists, they bound and stayed bleeding from nose and mouth ; moreover, it was a well-established remedy for cramp, Lord Bacon himself testifying that a limb suffering from cramp would be cured if bands of green Periwinkle were tied round it ; and William Coles, in his " Adam in Eden " (1657), gives a definite case of a friend who was " vehemently tormented with the cramp for a long while which could be by no means eased till he had wrapped some of the branches hereof about his limbs." Fourthly, superstition declared that it could unite man and wife in bonds of affection, for, as Culpepper pointed out three hundred years ago, " Venus owns

Wild Flowers as They Grow

this herb and saith, ' That the leaves eaten by man
and wife together cause love between them.' "
Moreover, the method of its growth is a method of
binding plant to earth, for its creeping rootstock
sends out long, trailing shoots, technically known
as " stolens," which, where the somewhat arched
shoot touches the ground, send out a rootlet from
a node, i.e. a point where a leaf arises, and bind the
shoot again to the earth. Later the intermediate
part of the arch dies away and a new plant starts
from the new rootlet. And since the plant is a
perennial the parent plant also lives and flourishes.
Thus does the Periwinkle cover the ground of moist
and shady woods " and creeping with his branches
far about," " quickly possesses a great compass."

The shoots are closely beset by pairs of little
plain, oval leaves, smooth, and of a very dark green
colour, which persist through the winter. The sap
within them is so acrid that the plant has been used
for tanning. Since the shoots trail on the ground
all the leaves are arranged so that they face the

The Lesser Periwinkle

sky and all get their full meed of sunshine, but should a branch turn upwards into a more or less erect attitude, then the leaves seek to arrange themselves in pairs at angles tending to a right angle, the angle being completely " right " when the stem is absolutely vertical. This is, of course, so that the leaves shall again get the fullest possible measure of light in the circumstances.

The pale, blue-purple flowers are of special charm and of very special interest. Each grows singly on a short stalk arising at a leaf-angle. The calyx is cut into five deep segments; the corolla forms a long tube below, expanding into a flat, five-lobed plate above—each petal lobe being square-tipped. The inside of the tube is pale in colour, and has a fringe of hairs at its mouth. Looking down into the flower the throat of the tube seems completely blocked, due to the very curious structure of stamens and stigma. The stamens are five in number, and set in a ring on the side of the tube about half-way up. Their five heads bend towards the centre,

13

Wild Flowers as They Grow

almost touching and forming a cupola ; each carries a hairy crest. Their filaments bend like a knee. The ovary at the base of (but inside) the petal tube is divided into two chambers, but has only a single style for the two ; this is an unusual thing. On either side of it are a couple of sparkling honey glands. The style, narrow at the base, enlarges like an inverted cone above, and is topped by a flat, round plate of unique description. Its circular edge glistens and is sticky, for this edge is the stigma. The "knees" of the stamen filaments come just below this plate. From the centre of the plate rises a brush of hairs. The diagram sets forth the structure in detail. And this is how the flower of the Lesser Periwinkle "works":

The anthers open on their inner side and the pollen falls on and into the brush of hairs of the stigma plate. It cannot, however, reach the sticky, receptive edge. An insect comes—bees and flies are frequent visitors—and though the honey is hidden at the base of the tube, eleven

The Lesser Periwinkle

millimetres away, yet it can get its head well into the tube, so that a proboscis but eight millimetres long can reach the nectar. It thrusts its head in—no doubt the " knee " allows each stamen to " give " a little ; its proboscis plunges into the honey ; as it withdraws it all smeared with nectar past the hairy brush on and in which pollen grains are lying, some must needs stick to it and be carried off. On going to another flower and plunging past the adhesive edge of the stigma plate, some of this pollen will be transferred to it, and thus fertilisation be effected. However, in spite of all this elaboration, the plant in this country rarely sets fruit. Hence it is some-times supposed not to be a native ; but probably the plant finds it more profitable to expend its energy on its rooting, trailing stems for the furtherance of its propagation. When it does fruit it forms two little pods, each containing three or four seeds.

There are two Periwinkles, the Larger and the Lesser, found wild in our country, but the right to the title of true Briton is challenged in both cases.

Wild Flowers as They Grow

They belong to the *Apocynaceæ* family, a family known wild to us in this country only through these two plants. Other members of it, however, such as the oleander, the stephanotis, the stapelia and the hoya are familiar enough in our greenhouses.

The Periwinkle may be found in flower at all times of the year except in dead winter. It is sometimes known as "Blue Buttons," "Cockles," "Sorcerer's Violet," "Hundred Eyes," "Dicky-Dilver," and "Sen-green" (i.e. evergreen). It is the "Perwinkle" of Gerard, and the "Pervenké" of Chaucer.

> "There sprange the violet al newe
> And fresh pervenké rich of hewe."

And it is bound up with Wordsworth's beautiful thought of flower-happiness :

> "Through primrose tufts, in that sweet bower,
> The periwinkle trail'd its wreaths ;
> And 'tis my faith that every flower
> Enjoys the air it breathes."

THE SNOWFLAKE

LEUCOJUM ÆSTIVUM

THE Snowflake, like the snowdrop, can only on sufferance claim to be a "wild flower" of Great Britain. It has crept into our flora, by stealth and under protest, as it were, and retains

a, sepals. *b*, petals. *c*, a stamen. *d*, ovary, thickened style, stigma.
e, section through ovary showing seeds.

its place because it is more difficult to say it should not be there than to say it may possibly have a right to be included. Still the *Gardener's Magazine* of 1836 reports, on the authority of Dr. Woodward, a surgeon and a "good botanist," that the Spring

Wild Flowers as They Grow

Snowflake was growing wild in immense quantities at Catholic Chapel, Hethe, Oxfordshire, and that, moreover, records were to hand showing that it had been established there for, at any rate then, over a century. But nowadays this species is only found wild in Dorsetshire. The Summer Snowflake of our picture, the only other British species, has often been reported as wild by the Thames and in other parts of south-eastern England, but the fact remains that, strictly speaking, the Snowflake is not a true native, but belongs to Italy in particular and southern and central Europe in general. Perhaps, again, like its relative the snowdrop, it was brought and planted here by the monks, nuns and other religious who had made the pilgrimage to Rome; and perhaps, too, from its great resemblance to its relative, it may even have at times shared in the odour of sanctity enveloping that plant.

And that reminds us that the name Snowflake is a modern one, invented for the plant by the botanist, William Curtis, at the end of the eighteenth

The Snowflake

century to distinguish it from the snowdrop. The
old name for both snowdrop and Snowflake was
Violet. Gerard calls the snowdrop " the Timely
flouring Violet," and the Snowflake " The many
floured great bulbous Violet," though in the 1623
edition of his work it is stated : " Some also call them
Snowdrop." Later writers, hampered by such a
terrible length of name, referred to it as the Summer
Snowdrop, until Curtis happily both shortened and
distinguished it by calling it the Snowflake.

Though the snowdrop and the Snowflake belong
to the same family, the *Amaryllideæ,* they are placed
in different genera, yet the difference between them
sounds very small. In the snowdrop the three
outer petals are always longer than the three inner
petals, while the anthers of the stamens are pointed
and open only at the tip to let out their pollen (we
remember the flower is inverted), while in the
Snowflake the petals are all about the same length
and the anthers open by long slits. But in reality
there is no difficulty in distinguishing between the

Wild Flowers as They Grow

plants at sight. The Snowflake is a much larger edition of the snowdrop, with much longer leaves— indeed, they may be a foot long—narrow, plain- edged and " keeled " at the back, much resembling the leaves of a daffodil, and appearing very early indeed in the spring. The flowers, too, are borne, several together, from two to six in a cluster, on very long, bare stalks ; in the snowdrop there is a solitary one from each bulb. At first the flower-bud is erect, but as it opens it droops over—a white bell with green markings. Each of the six petals is quite distinct, three in an outer ring, three in an inner. Each has a thick green mark at the tip, in addition to long, colourless streaks which all con- verge to the base of the flower. Six stamens hang inside the bell, and when the flower opens they spread so far away from the stigma that no self- fertilisation is possible. On top of the bell, above the white petals, is the very dark green ovary. (Before the flower drooped over, this was, of course, *below* the petals.) Inside the bell the surface of the ovary

The Snowflake

shows as a cushion of glistening tissue, but no free honey can be detected coming from it. But the most remarkable feature of the flower is the style, or ovary column, for the middle part of this swells out, narrowing again at the tip, and this swollen part, if not actually a nectar-secreting gland, as Sprengel thought, is undoubtedly spongy and contains sweet juices. To find the style functioning in this way is, indeed, a rare event, and at once gives a note of distinction to the flower.

The flower's chief visitors are honey bees and butterflies—it blooms much later than the snowdrop, not, in fact, until warmer May days—and these at once make for the style, hanging like a clapper in the middle of the bell. Its tip, the stigma, projects beyond the flower and touches them first, and thus is pollinated if any pollen from another Snowflake flower has been brought with them. Clinging to the style the insects rummage for honey, and finding none free in the flower they probably probe into the spongy, sweet-sapped parts and there extract the

Wild Flowers as They Grow

sugary juice as substitute. Meanwhile they are sprinkled with pollen, for this is lying loose in the opened anthers and only needs a slight jar to fall out through the pores at their tips. The flowers last a week or two, and then as they wither their stalks bend over and lie along the ground, the ovaries swell, and the fruits form as green capsules, which eventually open by three valves to allow the black, glossy seeds to escape.

The Snowflake is a bulb plant—that is, it springs from a bulb—in this case about the size of a chestnut. The bulb consists of a central axis—the stem—completely and thickly enclosed within fleshy, overlapping leaves. In these leaves the plant stores rich reserves of foodstuff, and this enables it to throw up its fine, long leaves even before winter is over. Every year a bulb buds off tiny bulbs from its side, and these grow to the size of their parent and start a new plant, and in this way the Snowflake propagates itself with greater ease and certainty than by its seeds. Before summer is far through

The Snowflake

the leaves have all fallen to the ground, and soon they die off and no hint of the Snowflake remains above ground. Only the bulbs and their offspring wait below for the autumn to pass, and for their call to awake as the days first begin to lengthen.

The name *Leucojum*, or *Leucoium* as it used to be written, is derived from the Greek word *leukos*, meaning " white," from the colour of the corolla. It gives us another instance of curious transposition of flower names, for " moderne " writers of James I.'s day denoted wallflower and stock gilliflower by this title. Tradition and romance do not seem to touch the Snowflake, while as to its " vertues " in the sense of the old herbalists, we can only repeat with an Elizabethan writer that " touching the faculties of these bulbous Violets we have nothing to say, seeing that nothing is set downe hereof by the antient Writers, nor anything observed by the moderne, onely they are maintained and cherished in gardens for the beautie and rarenesse of the floures and sweetnesse of their smell."

THE LUNGWORT

PULMONARIA OFFICINALIS

A PLANT of diversity : clusters of flowers of diverse colours, form of flowers diverse in diverse plants, leaves in the same individual of diverse shapes, and, to crown all, a plant of many

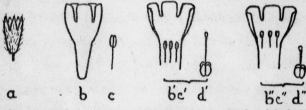

a, calyx. *b*, petals. *c*, stamen. *d'*, stigma, long style, four-lobed ovary. *d''*, stigma, short style, four-lobed ovary. *b' c' d'*, *b'' c'' d''*, the two forms of flower.

diverse names. Such is the Lungwort ! Rare as genuinely wild in Britain to-day, though common in central and southern Europe, it is still familiar enough to us in our gardens, and sometimes, too, as an " escape " in woods and pastures near them.

24

The Lungwort

Under the showers of April its opening flower-buds promise a rich rosiness of hue as they cluster, each on a short stalk, at the top of a main stem that is from half to a whole foot in height. The end bud opens first, the rest follow in succession. But as they open the rose-pink changes into blues and then purples, so that the stalk carries flowers of all colours as of all ages. This, of course, makes for greater conspicuousness where insects are concerned —and, indeed, for us, too—for the contrast of colour is the first thing we ourselves notice in the Lungwort. To this peculiarity it owes many of its country names, such as the apt " Soldiers and Sailors " (the red and blue), also " Adam and Eve," " Joseph and Mary," and " Joseph's Coat of Many Colours."

The stage of colouring may perhaps serve as a signal to visiting insects, thus Hermann Müller, watching, saw that a certain kind of bee (*Anthophora pilipes*) only visited flowers in the red stage, always passing over those in the blue. This change of colour is also a characteristic of others in the same

Wild Flowers as They Grow

family—the family of the *Boraginaceæ*—in the forget-me-not to a slight extent, and in the viper's bugloss to a greater. Further, as they open the flowers droop, and thus protect their pollen and their honey from rain and cold, and since they hang rather like a bunch of cowslips a very old name for the plant was "Cowslip" with various qualifications, such as "Cowslip of Jerusalem" (Gerard's name), or "Bedlam Cowslip," because of the fantastic colouring, or "Bugloss Cowslip," because of its resemblance to its relative, the aforementioned viper's bugloss.

All the flowers have a rather long and rough calyx, with five teeth at the top. This necessitates a tube to the corolla, which, above, however, expands into a cup with five lobes. In the bud these lobes are most neatly folded inwards, covering over the so-called "essential" organs. Five small stamens stand on the corolla tube, their dark heads containing silvery pollen. But as we investigate further we are aware of divergences. Sometimes the

The Lungwort

stamens are set high up in the tube, sometimes low down. Also, though there are four nutlets at the base of each flower, the stylar column that rises from between them is sometimes short and sometimes long. Where the stamens are set high in the tube there the style is short ; where they are set low down there it is tall. So botanists say the Lungwort (like the primrose) is dimorphic—that is, it has flowers of two forms. The stamens curve inwards, and a tuft of hairs is between each, so that the opening into the somewhat wide petal-tube is narrowed. The hairs also protect the honey, which is plentifully produced in four glands at the base of the ovary and then stored at the bottom of the corolla.

The appearance of the flowers in early spring days when they are not likely to be unduly challenged by brilliant neighbours, the bizarre colouring, the lavish honey, all attract many visitors of the bee and the butterfly classes, and since the basin of the flower allows an insect to get its head well in, even those with the shorter probosces can reach the honey in the depth. Nature's plan is for the insects to carry the pollen from the anthers high up in the tube to the stigma on top of the long style in another plant, and for the pollen from the low-down anthers to be taken to a short-styled plant. Obviously the relative positions of these various parts are such as to make this cross-fertilisation almost inevitable, since that part of the insect's body that receives pollen from the high rank of stamens will be the very part that touches the tip of the long style, and similarly for the short stamens and the short style.

Many experiments have, however, been made to see what other possibilities there are, notably by Hildebrand nearly fifty years ago. He obtained no seed if the flowers were self-pollinated, nor yet if long- and short-styled flowers received their pollen from flowers of their own type. By crossing them as Nature intended he got the natural amount of seed. Kerner, however, does not agree with this statement; he states that the long-styled form may

The Lungwort

occasionally fertilise itself, failing legitimate cross-fertilisation. Lord Avebury, again, says that only the short-styled form can fertilise itself, and then only to produce a small quantity of seed ; but when we remember that the flower droops, and that in the long-styled form the anthers are *above* the stigma, and pollen from them must drop on it, Kerner's statement on the face of it seems more probable. Other observers have shown that if insects are excluded there is no fruit formed. But no doubt the truth is that the flower's mechanism works well on the proper lines laid down for it in the law of Nature, and very indifferently or not at all on any other lines.

Hildebrand also found that the first flower on the stalk to open had no seed, but probably this is because the flower-cluster was not then sufficiently advanced in colour to be attractive to insects. The fruit is four small, smooth nuts which, as an old writer said, are "lodged in the bosom of the permanent calyx."

The leaves are quite as noteworthy as the flowers.

Wild Flowers as They Grow

The flowering stalks carry small, almost stalkless leaves, but the mass of the plant's leaves consists of a big tuft rising straight from the root. The leaves are large, oval, stalked, and covered with rough hairs. In the bud they are the palest green, their two edges curling over so as to meet on the face along the midrib, while a thick coat of silvery hairs envelops them. Though they are unfolding they do not fully develop until after the flowers have gone. In the garden variety and in the "escapes" these leaves are very handsome and characteristic, for their dark surface is marked with blotches of greenish white. It is these blotches that give the plant its name of Lungwort, from their supposed resemblance to diseased lungs. "Gooseberry Fool" (green gooseberries and white cream), "Our Lady's Milkwort" (resemblance to spilt drops of milk), "Spotted Mary" and "Spotted Comfrey" are other "aspect" names of this stage. In the truly wild British Lungwort these radicle leaves are narrower and less handsome, often having no spots upon them. Dr. Thornton's

The Lungwort

" Herbal " of just a century ago, however, speaks of the Spotted Lungwort as "a plant common enough in hedges and in shady and rather moist situations. . . . From its beauty it has obtained a place in our gardens."

The leaves had some medicinal reputation for diseases of the lungs, but not so much as is often believed. The "Lungwort" of our remoter ancestors was really a moss. The chief use of these leaves was as a pot-herb; thus Lyte, writing in Queen Elizabeth's day, tells us that " this plant hath no great use in physicke, but is used in meate and sallades, with eggs." In the north their use as a culinary vegetable still lingers.

Certain homely names for the plant are difficult to account for, such as " Sage of Bethlehem," and " Sage of Jerusalem," both of which were once common, also " Beggar's Basket," and " Bottle-of-all-sorts."

THE LILY OF THE VALLEY

CONVALLARIA MAJALIS

THE Lily of the Valley is a poet's flower. After the rose it shares with the violet and the cowslip the distinction of being prime favourite,

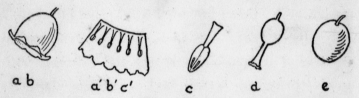

a b, bell of sepals and petals.   *a′ b′ c′*, stamens on bell.   *c*, a stamen.
d, ovary, style, stigma.   *e*, berry.

indeed, there are even those who brook no rival to it, and whose feelings are voiced by Keats :

> " No flower amid the garden fairer grows
> Than the sweet lily of the lowly vale,
> The Queen of Flowers."

All the charms of flowerhood seems to centre in it.

The Lily of the Valley

Its apparent shrinking from notice—

> " That shy plant—the lily of the vale—
> That loves the ground, and from the sun withholds
> Her pensive beauty, from the breeze her sweets "
>
> *(Wordsworth.)*

and yet, when found, the magic of its beauty and the enchantment of its scent give it an individuality so alluring that, according to the personification of the poetic imagination—

> " We might believe . . .
> That thou wert once a maiden, meek and good,
> That pined away beneath her native wood
> For very fear of her own loveliness,
> And died of love she never would confess."
>
> *(Hartley Coleridge.)*

Let us briefly run through the life-story of this " Naiad of the Vale." In the dryer parts of woods —ash woods in particular—one may find it forming quite extensive societies. In early spring days the creeping rhizome (underground stem) sends up quill-like shoots emerging from a scaly sheath. As they lengthen and uncoil they prove to consist of two leaves, one within another, rising directly from the

Wild Flowers as They Grow

rhizome. These have no stems, though their narrow-ing, curled foot-stalks almost look like such. Their plain, oval blades of somewhat concave surface slant a little backwards and catch all the rain possible, conducting it straight away through curling base, as through a spout, to the root.

At the back of the leaves, and rising also straight from the creeping rhizome, though lightly enclosed at the base in the same scaly sheath with them, is the flower stem. It is not quite so tall as they are, and is itself absolutely naked of leaves. In the earliest stage it bears at its summit a number of greenish buds, each on a very short stalk, the youngest at the tip. As the buds open they turn downwards and the flowers hang like a peal of fairy bells. "Ladder to Heaven" is a country name they have at this stage suggested. The Lily of the Valley should be in flower with the hawthorn, for careful experiment shows that both require exactly the same number of degrees of sun-warmth to bring them to maturity.

The Lily of the Valley

Sepals and petals alike are purest white, and together they form a plain bell whose edge turns back with six small scallops. The six little stamens are fastened inside near the top of the bell, and in the centre hangs the ovary with short, thick style and button stigma. The anthers open on to the inside of the bell, and are ready just a little before the stigma. The style is longer than the stamen filaments, so the stigma is below the anthers. There is no free honey in the little flowers, though a certain amount of sweet, juicy sap is stored in a tissue round the base of the ovary. But the intense fragrance leaves no need of nectar to advertise the flower. Legend says that it is the fragrance of the Lily of the Valley that draws the nightingale from hedge and bush and leads him to choose his mate in the recesses of the glade. It is said, too, to be almost unique among scents, only that of an odd Mexican cactus can be at all thought to resemble it. It is commonly reputed to be of the greatest value in nervous troubles and a most delightful antidote to headache ; on the other hand, a certain French scientist has recently propounded the theory that the fragrance of many flowers, and this Lily in particular, is very injurious to the voice, and he would bar all the offering of bouquets to singers —and, indeed, have the flowers banished entirely from their presence.

The bees are great visitors. As they approach the mouth of the bell they are bound first to strike the projecting stigma and smear it with any pollen they may bring ; but if the anticipated visit should fail the pollen is ultimately bound to fall on the edge of the stigma, which is roughened to retain it more easily, and so fertilisation is certain. The flowers pass into berries as the summer progresses, and September sees them hanging, in hue a most brilliant vermilion, each where a flower once was. " Our Lady's Tears," an old name for the plant and one still heard on the Continent, may be derived from these blood-red drops, or it may refer to the flowers in their purity of whiteness. Each berry

The Lily of the Valley

contains vermilion flesh round a pale, hard seed. But though the plant produces fruit, its persistent underground stem does most of its propagation.

The Lily of the Valley belongs, as its name implies, to the family of the Lilies, forming a special genus all to itself among them. It is, perhaps, most nearly akin to the Solomon's Seal, but it carries no leaves on its flower stalk as the latter does.

Special virtue was once supposed to lie in water distilled from the scented flowers. It was known as *Aqua aurea* (" Golden Water "), and was deemed worthy to be kept in vessels of gold and silver. Coles (1657) tells us how it was prepared. " Take the flowers and steep them in New Wine for the space of a month ; which being finished, take them out again and distill the Wine three times over in a Limbeck. This Wine is more precious than gold ; for if any one that is troubled with Apoplexy drink thereof with six grains of Pepper and a little Lavander water they shall not need to fear it that moneth." Rembertus Dodonæus (circa 1560), pointed out how this water "doth strengthen the Memorie" and "comforteth the Harte," while much about the same time Joachimus Camerarius, a renowned physician of Nuremberg, gave a similar prescription quoted by Gerard—"That a Glasse being filled with the flowers of May Lillies and set in an Ant Hill with the mouth close stopped for a month's space, and then taken out, ye shall find a liquor in the glasse which being outwardly applied helps the gout very much." Also, it was greatly valued against infectious fevers.

There are various pretty and curious old names for this plant, such as "Lilly-Convally," and its variations "Convall Lilly," "Liriconfancy," or "Lilly-Confancy."

The Lily of the Valley is very local as a wild flower. In certain districts of England it is still to be found in abundance, but in many it is quite unknown. It no longer, alas! "groweth plentifully upon Hamstead heath four miles from London,"

The Lily of the Valley

as Gerard saw it in Queen Elizabeth's days, and tradition says that it vanished when the trees on the heath were cut down. But at the beginning of last century it was still very plentiful in the woods of Norwood. Legend accounts for the flower in Sussex by recounting how St. Leonard fought against a dragon in the woods there and only after many fierce and bloody encounters did the saint triumph. But wherever his blood fell there Lilies of the Valley sprang up in remembrance of the fight.

These lilies have recently figured largely in experiments relating to the forcing of plants by means of anæsthetics, such as chloroform and ether. It has been found that their winter buds, placed in the vapour of chloroform for a few hours and then planted, break into leaf and flower considerably before those not so treated. Moreover, in the experiments, the resulting plants were exceptionally fine.

THE TWAYBLADE

LISTERA OVATA

ONLY two big, egg-shaped leaves—the "tway blades"—and a slender spike of insignificant flowers whose green colouring makes the children say: "They never come out," and yet a

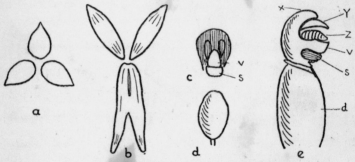

a, sepals.   *b*, petals, the lower one being the lip or labellum.   *c*, column, pollinia, rostellum, stigma (part view).   *d*, ovary.   *e* (after Hooker). *x*, column.   *y*, anther case.   *z*, pollinium.   *v*, rostellum.   *s*, stigma. *d*, ovary.

plant of such wonderful ways that Charles Darwin spoke of it as one of the most remarkable members

The Twayblade

of a family whose every member is itself wonderful. It is an orchid and a lover of damp, shady places, whether in wood or pasture, with a strong preference for limestone or chalky soil, and though reported from most parts of Britain it is said to be specially partial to Wales. Usually it is only a foot or so high, but if it find a spot exactly suited to it it may double this height. Below ground its roots are just a brown bundle of thickish fibres, and in this it differs from all other British orchids, for it has nothing of the nature of bulbs such as most of them have, it has not even the succulence of that mass of root-fibres that is the most striking characteristic of its closest relative, the *Neottia*, or Bird's Nest Orchid (*see* Vol. IV.). From the damp earth the single stem rises for, perhaps, some six inches ; it is thick, yellowish, and sheathed with a colourless bract or two. And then, almost opposite to each other, stretch two broad leaves, stalkless and vivid, and marked with outstanding veins that run from base to tip. No wonder that the stalk below is but a sickly green, for they must shade it from much of the sunlight, and hence from the power that would enable it to form green colouring matter.

But if the twin leaves are the outstanding characteristic of the plant, it is in those flowers so lacking in beauty that the chief interest lies, for each is an elaborate piece of plant mechanism. There are three ordinary sepals, green, ovate in shape, and with a sharp tip; the three petals are a lighter green, the two side ones being a slighter edition of the sepals, while the lowest petal is a long, spreading lip, its tip two-cleft. Above this cleft is a furrow running up the middle, and since honey oozes out of its banks it is a miniature river of nectar.

Now, the middle of the flower in an orchid has developed quite differently from that in any other flower. There is only one stamen, and it consists simply of a two-celled anther. The ovary is there certainly, lying outside the sepals and petals; its style has coalesced with the filament of the stamen, and the two form what is known as the "column."

The Twayblade

The " column " is sometimes spoken of as being " the prolongation of the floral axis." Normally, there should be three stigmas, but the two top ones go to form a remarkable organ known as the rostellum—no other plant has such an organ. The lower stigma alone functions as such, and is sticky. Therefore, looking straight into a flower of the Twayblade we have the column at the back, its upper part broad and protecting the anther, which is in front of it. Just below the anther the rostellum projects—in this orchid rather large and thin and somewhat scale-like, bulging in front and slightly arching over the stigma which lies below it. The anther contains in its two cells two masses of pollen —pollinia—the pollen grains being slightly held together by elastic strands. These cells open each by a slit in front, and through this slit falls the pollinium, which is rather like a skittle in shape. Its tip just catches the edge of the rostellum, and there, at the opening of the flower, the two lie side by side awaiting developments. The tissue of the rostellum is divided into a series of locules, each of which contains a drop of thin, milky fluid and possesses the power of violently exploding if touched. So sensitive is this organ that a touch from the thinnest human hair is sufficient to bring about the explosion, and thereupon two milky drops are shot out. Like some enamels, a film forms on them instantly, and in two or three seconds they are brown and " set." Notice that that edge of the rostellum on which the pollinia tip rests is *not* sensitive ; if it were the masses of pollen would be immediately glued permanently in the recesses of their own flower—the last thing the plant desires.

Let us now see by what means the mechanism is set working. The Twayblade is popular with beetles and small flies, who have not the æsthetic craving for colour that the bees and the butter-flies possess. They are quite content with insig-nificance and plainness if they can secure nectar, so they come in numbers to this plant—it is sometimes suggested that they must be drawn

44

The Twayblade

thither by an odour impalpable to our grosser senses. The beetle, let us say, alights on the cleft tip that is specially there for platform purposes. It crawls up the lip, licking, as it proceeds, the honey from the fairy-like trough. When it reaches the end just by the "column," it naturally lifts its head and so strikes the arching, and exquisitely sensitive rostellum. Out flies the necessary cement, touching both the pollinia and the insect's head. A second suffices for the one to be firmly glued to the other, and the insect backs out, taking the pollinia with it. But as a further result of the explosion the rostellum curves downwards over the sticky stigma, and thus, in the backing out, the pollinia cannot be placed upon it. Off flies the insect with its pollinia (sometimes having received them full in its eyes), and it may thus collect pair after pair if it go to one newly opened flower after another.

But if the stigma is now shielded by the rostellum, how can it receive pollen itself from another flower? Well, it does not remain shielded, for after a short time the rostellum moves again, leaving an open passage to it. At this point, too, it becomes very much stickier, and now a beetle, lapping along the nectar course with projecting pollinia horns, will strike the stigma with them. They crumble at once, and some of their pollen lies fast on the sticky surface. The beetle may again lift its head at the end of the furrow, but this time there is no explosion and no pollinia to annex, for the flower has completed the cycle of its plans. Not often, either, do they miscarry; for instance, on one fading flower-spike Darwin found every single flower had both dispatched its pollinia and received pollen in return, and hence was setting seed. He also noticed that spiders' webs were often woven over and about these plants; no doubt the spiders had discovered what an excellent fly neighbourhood they afforded.

As to the Latin name, *Listera ovata*, the "ovata," of course, refers to the egg-shaped leaves, and *Listera* is after a certain Dr. Martin Lister, who was physician to Queen Anne and a naturalist of some renown.

THE DOGWOOD

CORNUS SANGUINEA

"THE Cornell Tree that is planted in our orchards being the male (for the female is a hedge bush)." In this parenthesis Parkinson somewhat contemptuously alludes to the Dogwood.

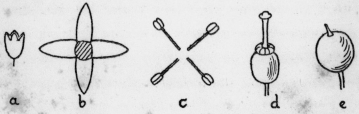

a, calyx. *b*, petals. *c*, stamens. *d*, stigma, style, honey gland, ovary.
e, fruit.

Presumably his epithets "male" and "female" only refer to the difference in size, for there is no other "sex" distinction to be noted. And yet the Dogwood is by no means to be despised, in spite of the fact that it does not attain quite to the height of

47

Wild Flowers as They Grow

that small, non-British tree the Cornel (*Cornus mas.*).
It often forms a handsome part of those composite
hedgerows that border old roads, and it is a true
native of our countryside. Twice in the year does
it add its quota of beauty to them ; once in early
summer days when its creamy, flat clusters of
flowers do a little, in a somewhat prim way, to fill
in the blank that the passing of the glory of the
snowy hawthorn always leaves ; and secondly, in
autumn time, when its foliage dyes with depths of
rich crimson and red-purple tones that the trees
may emulate but cannot surpass, those autumn
days when—

> " Every woodland tree is flushing like the dogwood,
> Flashing like the whitebeam, swaying like the reed ;
> Flushing like the dogwood, crimson in October,
> Streaming like the flag reed south-west blown.
> Flashing as in gusts the sudden lighted whitebeam,
> All seem to know what is for heaven alone."
>
> (*Swinburne.*)

For these hues is the Dogwood's specific name—
Sanguinea—given to it.

The Dogwood

Though mostly but a shrub it may rise to as much as fourteen or fifteen feet in height. Its wood is hard and horn-like, hence the generic name *Cornus* (Latin, a horn), and its use for ramrods, cog-wheels and skewers. Hence, too, its country name of " Prickwood " and " Skewer-wood " ; even its very name, Dogwood, is ultimately referable to this quality. And this in spite of the fact that inventive geniuses have asserted that it is called Dogwood because a wash made from its leaves was good for mangy dogs ; and in spite of the still more brilliant suggestion of Parkinson that it was called Dogwood because its astringent berries were *not* fit even for dogs ! " Dog " is really derived from the old English *dagge*—a dagger—and the Anglo-Saxon *dalc* or *dolc*, a brooch pin. It was undoubtedly the wood our Anglo-Saxon forbears used for their " dags " or goads, since it was tough and hard, and so its name came down to us as Dogwood, or, as it should be, " Dagwood." And this view is borne out by the fact that in some parts of the

country it has the synonyms " Gatter," or " Gaiter,"
or " Gadrise," derivatives of the Anglo-Saxon *gad-
treow*, a goad-tree.

The old branches of the shrub are covered with
brown bark scored with cracks, but the young
shoots of the spring are a bright crimson, and a
truly worthy support for the glossy, handsome
leaves. Now, one may always know a Dogwood by
its leaves, for they are a broad oval with sharp tip,
and carry most characteristic veining, to wit a
central midrib from which run three or four pairs
of strongly marked lateral veins, that curve in
more or less parallel fashion towards the tip. Each
leaf has a short stalk and stands with a fellow in
pairs along the stems. The individual pairs are
arranged on the stem in such a way that they always
get the maximum of sunlight. Hence on a horizontal branch they all lie on the same horizontal
plane; in a vertical branch each pair is at right
angles to the stem, and at right angles, too, to the
pair above and below, while on branches at inter-

The Dogwood

mediate angles the leaf-pairs take up corresponding intermediate positions.

The Dogwood is one of those plants that make small flowers, inconspicuous in themselves, a noticeable feature by massing them together. Individually each little flower has its tiny sepals united with the ovary wall, only their four teeth appearing. Its four white petals form a severe-looking cross. Between the petals four small stamens stretch like tiny rays. The little ovary contains two chambers, a potential seed in each, and it carries a single, rather thick style. The chief feature of the flower is the glistening honey gland, which forms a collar round the base of the style and a shining centre to the flower. A slight scent like that of the hawthorn clings about the clusters. This scent seems to be specially attractive to small flies, and it is these that chiefly form the Dogwood's visiting circle. They crawl over the clusters, licking up the honey pools that lie so invitingly exposed in every blossom, and, incidentally, trail the pollen from flower to flower and carry it from cluster to cluster.

The anthers open on the inside at the same time as the stigma matures to receive pollen, so no doubt both self- and cross-fertilisation happen. But, since the anthers at the end of the filament rays are situated some distance from the stigma, they would rub on the opposite side of the insect's body to that on which the stigma would rub, so that it is very likely an insect would place foreign pollen on the stigma before any of the flower's own would reach it. In the event of no insect coming the stamens rise from their almost horizontal position and stand over the stigma, thus ensuring self-fertilisation.

The flower clusters fade, the ovaries swell into green berries that, as September comes, turn to a black-purple, each on its crimson stalk, and form noticeable groups. There is not really much juiciness about these berries, for they contain a horny pill of a seed almost as large as the berry itself; at one time an oil was manufactured from them which

The Dogwood

gave a serviceable light in lamps. Soap of a certain value can also be made from them. Their juice is extremely acrid and staining. These berries are very reminiscent of those of the ivy, and, indeed, the families of the ivy and the Dogwood are closely akin. Closely akin, too, is the family of the honeysuckle. The *Cornaceæ*—to which the Dogwood belongs—is but a very small family and only known in Europe through the various *Cornus* species. Only two are wild in this country, the Dogwood and the Dwarf Cornel, the latter being just a little herb, with the tiniest white clusters, each more like a single flower, and the minutest of purple berries.

One of the many superstitions connected with St. John's Eve centres round the Dogwood. It is firmly held in Prussian country-lore that if one's handkerchief be allowed to absorb the sap of the Dogwood on that night all one's hopes and desires will be fulfilled.

THE YELLOW RATTLE

RHINANTHUS CRISTA-GALLI

AN extraordinary looking plant of sinister
countenance, an individual that at once
raises a feeling of suspicion in the mind! Ruddy,
thin, square stems up to a foot in height, leaves that

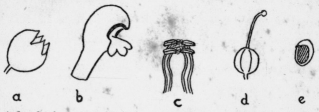

a, inflated calyx. *b*, corolla. *c*, stamens with matted hairs. *d*, stigma,
style, ovary. *e*, seed, slightly winged.

are stalkless triangles set opposite to one another
in pairs upon the stem and cut into great jagged
teeth, and spikes of bright yellow, hooded flowers of
peculiar outline make it up. The substance of the
leaves is harsh and their surface is covered with

The Yellow Rattle

minute, rigid hairs all pointing tipwards, so that it is impossible to pass the leaf from apex to base across one's lips without great unpleasantness, though it will run smoothly enough along the lip over the hairs if the direction be reversed. This characteristic is to prevent small, wingless insects intent on rifling honey or pollen, from creeping along the leaves to the stem and so up to the flowers.

The bracts or leaves at the base of the flowers are still more jagged than the leaves, and it is to them that it owes its specific name, *Crista-galli,* or " cock's comb," a name that it carries in other countries besides ours. Perhaps, too, the shape of the flower, with its fanciful suggestion of the head of a fowl, has emphasised its association with the idea of a cock, and then by easy transference of thought to St. Peter, and since it is in the zenith of its flowering about St. Peter's Day—June 29th— it was in olden days taken as the flower of that festival. " The yellow floure, called the Yellow Cockscombe, which floureth now in the fields is a

Wild Flowers as They Grow

sign of St. Peter's Day whereon it is always in fine floure in order to admonish us of the denial of our Lord by St. Peter," said an old writer.

The most remarkable feature of the flower is, perhaps, the great inflated calyx, like a flattened bladder, ending in four small teeth. This inflation no doubt prevents thieving bees from getting at the honey by boring, but its main service to the plant comes later when the seeds have to be dispersed. Out of the bladder and beyond the four teeth rises the great hooded corolla, with a very thick tube as a neck, which is hidden within the calyx. Under the hood in front are a couple of purple teeth— just a dark edge—to point out the opening. Below the teeth is a platform of three frilly lobes. Thus the corolla is of the two-lipped variety so usual in the *Scrophulariaceæ* family to which the plant belongs. Inside, and right under the hood, are two pairs of stamens, with white waved filaments and black heads, and each pair have their heads joined by white matted hairs, so that they form a flat

The Yellow Rattle

arch across the flower, and incidentally a very effective sprinkling apparatus. The anthers open on their inner faces, hence their white spheroidal pollen falls among the matted hairs and lies there ready for the critical moment. In the centre of the flower is a flat, almost circular ovary bulging a little with seeds within. A long column from it curves round closely under the hood, and just puts its tip out of the opening above the purple teeth. In front of the ovary is a projection of the fleshy base, and it is here that honey forms.

Now, though the Yellow Rattle has many visitors, bees are those that it specially desires and for which it caters. Müller, carefully watching, saw no fewer than nine different sorts of bee visit it. And this is the order of the day when a bee pays a call : it hovers before the flower and makes straight for the purple-outlined opening under the hood, alighting on the firm, frilly platform of the lower lip, which is well able to bear the weight. Its head immediately touches the delicate projecting tip of the ovary column just above. Any pollen on its head is thus transferred. But to get to the honey manufactured in the lobe of the ovary and stored in the corolla tube it must dive under the two narrow arches of the anther pairs, and between the curving, stiff, filament columns that support them. These are rudely shaken, and out falls the pollen from the matted hairs like water from a shower-bath, sprinkling the insect in a line on the top of its head, exactly where the stigma had just rubbed and precisely where the stigma in the next flower will rub later. The bee is bound to keep in a straight line when entering the flower, because the stamen filaments are beset with sharp spines that prevent it straying. Also the sprinkling cannot be promiscuous, since a fringe of hairs on the lower edge of the anthers on either side keeps the pollen shower confined between them. Later the style curls downwards and inwards to its own stamen for self-fertilisation if necessary.

When the flower is fertilised the corolla drops off,

The Yellow Rattle

leaving behind the inflated and still-growing calyx, looking now like a closed purse—there may be a dozen of them arranged down the stem. In Jutland the peasants call the plant "Löki's Purse." Since Löki is the personification of malice and subtlety, we have again the suggestion of something sinister arising, a suggestion justified, as we shall see. The "purses" now rapidly lose their greenness and become dry and scaly and rustle and rattle in the wind. Hence the names "Yellow Rattle" and "Rattle-boxes" for the plant. "When the Yellow Rattle rattles then the hay is ripe," say the Swedes. By August all that is left of the vivid yellow and green herb of St. Peter is a pale, death-like spike, which looks like a ghost and recalls a chattering skeleton. "Penny Grass" and "Hen-penny," calling to mind the days of silver pence, are old country names derived from the aspect of the plant at this stage.

But it is not very easy for seeds—even though they each possess a circular wing of their own—

Wild Flowers as They Grow

to get out of a purse like this, which opens only at the top, especially as they are also in an inner, though also open, purse—the ovary—so here the bladdery calyx comes to the rescue. It catches the wind with considerable force, and rocks to and fro vehemently whenever there is a breeze. Out jerk occasional seeds which are caught by the same gust, and so, aided by their own wings, they are carried away and scattered, though not to any great distance. Indeed, the young plants are generally found growing close round their parent, and regular colonies of considerable size are formed—"It might have been sown by the bushel," remarks Kerner.

But if one watches the growth of one of these seedlings, one becomes aware that the Yellow Rattle has a secret sin, one that, though hidden, cannot be completely concealed. It has strong leanings towards parasitism. At first the little plant, aided by a good stock of reserve material provided by the parent, makes a brave start on a life of independence, but soon it puts out from

The Yellow Rattle

its roots below ground rounded suckers of some size with thickened margins, and these lay themselves on the roots of the grass or of other plants that may be near, and gripping the root round, perhaps half its circumference, draw from it by means of many absorption cells the rich sap that it has provided for its own use.

The Yellow Rattle, to be quite fair to it, does not depend wholly upon the other plant ; it is not a complete parasite, or it would not have such fine gay leaves and flowers ; it does part of its own work in building foodstuffs from the salts and water of the soil and the gases in the air, but it supplements its income in this illegitimate way. For a long time the true nature of the plant was quite unsuspected, though it had always been eyed with disfavour and considered to injure the meadows ; where it grew in any abundance farmers said it "burned" their grass, and an Elizabethan writer remarks : "It grows in dry medowes and pastures, and is to them a great anoyance." But in 1847

Wild Flowers as They Grow

a French botanist, a M. Decaisne, hazarded the suggestion that the plant, albeit green, was a parasite, a somewhat startling proposition to British botanists, since at that time our parasites were supposed to be always brown and leafless—the mistletoe excepted. But experiments proved the suggestion correct; the Yellow Rattle could not flourish if it were grown away from the neighbourhood of other plants, being stunted, almost flowerless, and quite seedless in those circumstances. Nowadays we are fully aware that the family *Scrophulariaceæ*, as represented in Great Britain, has within its borders five groups of plants that are semi-parasites, namely (1) the three bartsias, (2) the eye-bright (described in Vol. III.), (3) the Yellow Rattle, (4) the red rattle (*also see* Vol. III.), and the meadow lousewort, (5) the four cow-wheats; and all of these attempt to get a living more easily by filching from their neighbours.

THE IVY-LEAVED TOADFLAX

LINARIA CYMBALARIA

THE awkward, ugly, English name ill befits a little plant of such delicacy and charm. Scarcely better, either, is " Mother of Thousands," the name by which our country folk often know it,

a, calyx.   *b*, petals (side view).   *b'*, petals (front view) showing mounds.
c, stamens.   *d*, stigma, style, ovary.   *e*, fruit capsule.

and which has special reference to the apparently unending succession of bright little flowers that it produces from spring to autumn. Far more sympathetic and appreciative is the name given to it by its own countrymen of Italy, who term it the " Herb of the Madonna," and dedicate it to her

Wild Flowers as They Grow

because of its grace and beauty. As is the case with so many of the very attractive plants that to-day we gather wild, we cannot actually claim it as a Britisher, for it came to us from the southern countries of Europe in comparatively recent times. In the sixteenth century it was counted as purely a plant for cultivation, but being very hardy and adaptable it has since completely naturalised itself, and is no longer to be classed among the aliens.

Clinging to the mortar of some old wall, and flourishing happily where the conditions of life seem most precarious and ascetic, its slender, trailing stems droop gracefully over the stones, here and there sending out little rootlets from the nodes so that no opportunity may be lost of strengthening its hold. The delicate, smooth stems carry delicate, picturesque and also perfectly smooth leaves that, with their five-rounded lobes, recall certain of the less angular ivy leaves—hence its common name. Some of the leaves, even when full grown, are very small—the wall does not offer

The Ivy-Leaved Toadflax

a luxuriant living—but where more soil has collected in the crannies they may be as much as a couple of inches across. Though on the face they are a shining, vivid green, on the back they are pale and dull, and often tinted with purple. To the taste they are slightly acrid, but they possess no medicinal quality, though once they had an unenviable notoriety. In the earlier days of the eighteenth century a Neapolitan woman, named Tophania, concocted and sold a secret poison which came to be known as " Poudre de Succession." Its administration caused the victim to die a lingering death, as though of some slow disease, and it is said that some six hundred people died from its effects before the arch-poisoner was found out. An analysis of " Poudre de Succession " made by the physician to Charles V., King of the Two Sicilies, showed that it consisted of a liquid known as *Aqua Cymbalariæ*, made from the leaves of the Ivy-leaved Toadflax, in which was dissolved some compound of arsenic. It was, of course, the arsenic, not

Wild Flowers as They Grow

the little Toadflax, that was at the root of the mischief.

All through the summer the lilac flowers follow one another; as one fades another takes its place. They are held well forward on long stalks, "face on" to the sunshine, and it is at first difficult to realise that the bright, five-petalled flower with the light centre is identical in structure with the great Yellow Toadflax of the hedges, and almost identical with that of the snapdragon. But if the flower be turned about, it will be seen that the petals form the same sort of closed box, while an experimental pinching will make it "yawn" in the selfsame way. The only difference between the snapdragon and the Toadflax is that in the latter the lower part of the corolla runs backwards as a long spur, while in the snapdragon such a possibility is only indicated.

Let us notice closely the structure of this re-markable two-lipped corolla.

The upper lip is small and dark purple in colour; the two lobes that stand erect at the mouth of the

The Ivy-Leaved Toadflax

flower speak of the fact that two out of the five
petals combine to form it. These lobes are streaked
with a few purple lines, or " honey-guides." The
lower lip is much larger. Three petals make it up
and their three tips turn downwards as three pale-
lilac lobes. A third of the way back it hinges with
the upper lip to form a tube, and after passing the
point of insertion of the stem forms the aforementioned spur. Above the three lobes two big,
pale yellow mounds divided by a groove arise, and
are a capital alighting platform for an insect. If
we make the flower " yawn," we can see down its
throat and note that two rows of orange-coloured
hairs run back from the mounds and outline a
channel, while there is a small tuft of hairs by the
hinge on either side of the cavity. The orange
hairs on the floor of the throat cavity keep the
insect's head directed upwards, those on either side
prevent it straying from the straight path. Up
above in the roof are four stamens, their white
heads in two pairs, one pair in front of the other.

Wild Flowers as They Grow

They are open and showing their white pollen. Between them runs the style from the little ovary at the bottom of the tube. At the base of this minute ovary is a gland which secretes honey, and this trickles along a groove between the stamens into the spur, and is there collected. Both stamens and stigma seem to mature at the same time.

Cross-fertilisation can only be brought about by some insect, chiefly one of the smaller bees, settling on the mounds. The closed mouth of the flower promptly opens under the weight, and the insect inserts its long proboscis into the cavity in search of the honey in the spur. Its head will inevitably strike the pollen-dusty anthers in the roof, and so, when it flies away, it carries pollen on its head as well as honey in its pouch. As it backs out of the cavity the flower snaps to again.

But the most remarkable thing happens as the flower fades. Its stalk, hitherto so bravely holding out the flower, draws back under the leaves, and as the seed capsule forms and ripens it actually curves

The Ivy-Leaved Toadflax

towards the wall and is only arrested by coming into contact with it. The capsule is thus placed in some nook or crevice. It is a most extraordinary instinct that causes it to act thus—a measure of sheer self-preservation, indeed—for, if the capsule were held out as the flower was, when it burst and released its tiny black seeds they would all fall to the ground and, as the offspring of a parent whose home is a wall, be lost to posterity. As it is, the little seeds lie in the crevice, and since they are ridged and roughened on the surface, they do not easily slip out of it.

This little Toadflax has figured prominently and happily on one or two occasions. It is said that when Linnæus as a young man came to Oxford he, as the disturber of botanical tradition, was received somewhat coldly by the senior botanists there. But as he walked in the college garden with several dons interested in botany, masses of this plant on the garden wall caught their eye. Dillenius, the senior professor, stopped and spoke of various difficulties

he had recently found in connection with it.
Linnæus, however, was able at once to explain
them so clearly away that the professor's coldness
and prejudice were broken down, and admiration
for the young Swede took their place.

Again, a plant of the Ivy-leaved Toadflax was
once used to point a moral to the Chancellor of the
Exchequer. In 1850 a deputation approached him
with reference to abolishing that most unpopular
and iniquitous tax—the Window Tax. To illustrate
their contention that the blocking out of light was
a direct injury to health and prosperity, they produced an Ivy-leaved Toadflax, part of which had
grown with full access to the sunlight and part of
which had been accidentally cut off from such
access. The well-lighted portion was flourishing,
with fine leaves, flowers and seeds, the light-starved
portion was weak, small, flowerless and fruitless.
The argument was most telling, the Chancellor of
the Exchequer rational, and the tax-resisters gained
their point.

THE KIDNEY VETCH

ANTHYLLIS VULNERARIA

THE Kidney Vetch, after all, is not really one of the Vetches in spite of its name. It is true that it belongs to their family—the *Leguminoseæ* —but it is not included in the *Vicia*, or Vetches,

A, outer green bract. *a*, calyx. *b*, petals. *c*, stamens, filaments united.
d, ovary, style, stigma.

group of that family. It has not the tendrils that the vetches have, and its stamens are all joined together into one bundle, instead of the top stamen being free, and so leaving a gap in the filament tube, as is the case in its name-

Wild Flowers as They Grow

sakes. In fact, the Kidney Vetch has a unique personality of its own in various directions, and stands quite alone as the sole representative in our flora of the genus *Anthyllis*, a genus that at the best is but small, its twenty or so species being confined to the north temperate region of the Old World.

It is a low herb, from a few inches to a foot in height, and is often half sprawling on the ground. It loves the tops of cliffs, both sandstone and chalk, as well as the dry pastures of the chalky downs. Its foliage is not very much in evidence in the low herbage among which it dwells, for each leaf is cut up into a number of very narrow leaflets. The terminal leaflet is much longer and somewhat wider than the lateral ones, while the latter are often arranged very unevenly. But if the foliage is insignificant the flower clusters in June and July are very striking and quite unmistakable, for these consist of some fifteen to twenty flowers apiece, gathered into close heads, each head being set in a

The Kidney Vetch

big, circular, green ruff formed of a single green
bract which is cut deeply into many lobes. The
fact that these close clusters—" spoky rundles," in
Gerard's quaint phraseology—are somewhat kidney-
shaped no doubt accounts for the " Kidney " in its
common name, albeit Lyte, in his " Niewe Herball "
of 1578, says that the plant owns its name because
" it shall prevayle much against the strangury and
against the payne of the reynes." But other
herbalists do not generally appear to endorse this
statement. Gerard specially says it is " not used in
meate or medicine that I know of," and, probably,
as was so often done in those illogical days, Lyte
argued the cure from the name, and not the name
from the cure. Nevertheless, the plant had a definite reputation as a staunch-wound, and we have
on record that at the beginning of the eighteenth
century it was publicly sold for this purpose in
the market at Dublin under the name of "Stanch."
From this reputation, its specific botanical name of
Vulneraria (Latin, *vulnus*, a wound) was derived,

Wild Flowers as They Grow

also its old English names of "Stanch" or
"Staunche," and "Woundwort."

If we look closely into the "spoky rundles," we
see that each of the fifteen to twenty stalkless
flowers has a bright yellow pointed end passing
back into a long, woolly tube. "They look like
lambs' tails," say the country children, and so as
"Lambs' Tails" they are often known. Likewise
as "Ladies' Fingers," with perhaps a reference to
such fingers in warm winter mittens, though this
name is sometimes attributed to the presence of
the spreading palmate bract at the back of the
flower-clusters. As we pick out individual flowers
from their setting they feel warm and woolly to the
touch, this being due to the coat of soft, white
hairs that so thickly envelops the calices. Though
the whole plant is covered with a slight down, it is
these calices that are the "downiest" part, and it
is they that account for the name *Anthyllis*, which
is derived from two Greek words signifying "flower"
and "down." Since each calyx is somewhat inflated,

74

The Kidney Vetch

it is a prominent part of the flower. The value of this down to a low herb is obvious. It prevents small insects from roaming at will over its surface —or, at any rate, makes it very difficult for them to do so. The petals are five, yellow just where they show beyond the calyx, but continuing back into the calyx tube as long, narrow, white limbs. It is rather as though they were all on stilts. The big, upper petal turns back with upstanding flap ; at the base of this flap, on either side, are two curved arms, very like those of an arm-chair, and these arms embrace the waist of the rest of the flower. The two side petals, or wings, are closely pressed together and enfold two still smaller ones which form the keel. At the base of the yellow portion of the wings, and on the upper side, are two fine hooks which need careful looking for. These fit into folds on either side of the keel and interlock these two portions of the flower. The keel wraps up the upper part of the ten stamens whose filaments are all joined to form a long white tube, though their heads are distinct. The pollen from these heads must necessarily fall into the cavity of the keel. At the base of the calyx lies a minute, green pod, very flattened and almost circular in outline, and from it a long style runs to the farthest point of the keel.

Now, since the tube of this flower is unusually long all short-tongued insects are barred from visiting it to any advantage to themselves; only butterflies and long-tongued bees can reach into its recesses to get the honey present. They alight upon the saddle ridge formed by the interlocked wings and keel, their weight depressing it. As the keel "gives," the pollen lying loose within is forced out through its apex by the stamens and style acting as a piston, and the grains scatter over the insects' abdomens and legs. Under a lens these grains can be seen to be all short, six-sided prisms with striated angles. When the flower is young the top of the style—the stigma—is quite dry, so that none of the pollen adheres to it, and the explosion

The Kidney Vetch

may occur several times over. But as the flower
ages and becomes limper, eventually the keel is
depressed to such an extent that the style shoots
out through the orifice and itself strikes the insect.
By this time it has become moist and sticky from
being rubbed, and it will gather on itself any
pollen that may be on that insect at the point it
strikes. This will almost certainly be pollen from
another neighbouring flower, since its own pollen
will have been dissipated by the previous explosions.
The whole arrangement is a very neat one. We
saw a similar one in the bird's foot trefoil (*Lotus
corniculatus*), described in Vol. I.

Among the flower's visitors a certain beautiful
little blue butterfly, by name *Polyommalus Hylas*,
is particularly constant and appreciative, but she
finds a special purpose for our Kidney Vetch, for
she lays her eggs in the ovary when she visits, and
thus makes an exchange for her own ends when she
flies off as carrier of the flower's pollen. The eggs
produce caterpillars, which find food in the immature

Wild Flowers as They Grow

seeds by their side. Later they crawl out and
retire below ground, and there remain for their
chrysalis stage—and, indeed, until they emerge in
their full glory as dainty blue butterflies. The
flower contains no honey, and has no appreciable
scent; it relies, therefore, upon its masses of colour
for attractive power.

As the flower fades, its petals change from yellow
through orange to brown, and this colour change
gives the Kidney Vetch in the mass a still more
striking appearance, for yellow, orange and brown
clusters rank side by side. The calyx becomes even
more inflated, and within, as in a bladder, the tiny
pod ripens. Eventually the dried-up clusters dis-
integrate, and the individual parts fall to the ground;
the wind catches the hairy, dry calyx bladders and
hustles them about, and thus their contents—the
pod with its usually single seed—get dispersed.

The Kidney Vetch bears on its roots in a marked
degree those little nodules which we now know are
the dwelling places of bacteria. These bacteria

The Kidney Vetch

receive benefit from, and return benefit to, the plant. They receive a home, and in return they take free nitrogen from the air and pass it on after combining it in such a way that the plant can use it in its physiological processes. Were it not for these bacteria the great reservoir of free nitrogen in the atmosphere would be sealed to the plant, and it would have to rely entirely upon the soil for the supply of its necessary nitrogen. It is because these bacteria colonies frequent the roots of many of the members of this family of the *Leguminoseæ*, such as peas, beans, bird's foot trefoil, etc., that these members can actually enrich the land in which they grow instead of impoverishing it. It has been suggested at various times that the Kidney Vetch should be cultivated as a fodder plant, and it does appear to be very acceptable to cattle and a good pasture, but the suggestion seems never to have been taken up seriously.

THE RED VALERIAN

CENTRANTHUS RUBER

THE Red Valerian is a " butterfly flower "— that is to say, it is built on lines exclusively adapted to the butterfly family—in which, of course, moths are included—and it acts in the matter of

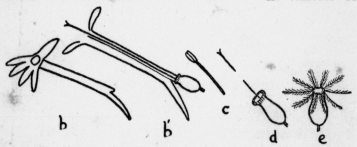

b, petals. *b'*, section through petal tube, showing division into larger and smaller tubes. *c*, the stamen. *d*, stigma, style, ovary with collar. *e*, fruit with feathery rays.

fertilisation after a unique and remarkable fashion peculiarly its own. Individually, the flowers are small but they stand, a number together, on the upper side of short branches at the top of a long stalk, and are massed, perhaps several hundred in all, into rounded pyramids. And inasmuch as they are of a rich ruby hue, and the plant loves to perch itself upon walls and rocks, they often form a ruddy crown to old castle battlements and ruined towers, or touch with rosy patches the dazzling whiteness of some chalk-pit side. The mass of colour, the richness of hue, set it apart from British plants with their colder colouring, and it is a fact that its true home is in more southern parts, but, like so many other members of the continental plant-world, it wandered to our island long ago, and has now made itself quite at home; yet not so very long ago after all as a " wilding," for Gerard only speaks of it as growing plentifully in his garden, " being a great ornament to the same and not common in England."

This vividness of appearance is responsible for many of its colloquial names, such as " Soldiers," " Fox's Brush " (form of pyramid plus colour), " Scarlet Lightning," and very probably " Drunken

Wild Flowers as They Grow

Sailor " or " Drunken Willies " (from the idea of " seeing red "). " Bouncing Bess " (of a ruddy countenance), " Pretty Polly " and " Pretty Mary," too, come from its gayness, while " American Lilac " or " German Lilac " speak of its massed pyramids. Its gorgeousness has sometimes led to its being spoken of as the parvenu of the plant world, but, after all, a plant with the gayest of possible colleagues in the insect world must needs dress accordingly.

At the base of each flower is a short, green seed-case like a pedestal with a ruby capital; on this is set a long, slender petal-tube which has a " tail " running down by the side of the seed-case. This " tail " or spur, causes the plant to be known as the " Spur Valerian "—the ordinary Valerian having no such spur. At the top the tube spreads into five petal lobes, one above and four, like the four fingers of a hand, below—a most exceptional arrangement. When the petals first open only the dark head of a solitary stamen see-sawing across its filament projects from the tube. Again, it is

The Red Valerian

rare to find a flower content with a single stamen. By the side of the stamen, but not so tall, is the red column from the ovary ; really this column is very long and the stamen filament very short, but the latter stands high up on the corolla tube while the former has to run right down through the length of the tube to the ovary beneath it. Now extremely narrow as is the corolla tube, not thicker, indeed, than an average pin, it is yet divided lengthwise into a smaller and a greater tube, as can be seen if it be cut across and looked at in section with a hand-lens. It is actually through the smaller of these tunnels that the ovary-column runs. The larger of the tunnels is lined with outstanding hairs and ends with the spur, and it is through this tunnel, therefore, that an insect must probe to reach the honey collected in that spur. And only the proboscis of a butterfly or a moth is long and fine enough to pass down so minute a channel.

Watch an opening flower. The stamen stands well out of it, the two compartments of the see-

Wild Flowers as They Grow

sawing anther are slitting lengthwise and exposing glittering grains of pollen. If a butterfly now delicately approaches it and thrusts its long proboscis through the appointed channel it must needs annex on its head some of these bright grains, and on departing carry them away. Other butterflies follow on in the sunshine, and more and more pollen is dispatched; but meanwhile the stamen has begun to bend over the edge of the corolla, while the ovary column is growing up into its place, and soon any butterfly sipping the nectar will strike the stigma and smear it with pollen instead of touching the anther, for the one has completely taken the place of the other. But the stamen has possibly not yet quite completed its work. It is hanging so far over the corolla edge that there is more than a chance it will drop pollen on to the stigma in an adjacent flower, so thickly are the flowers massed together. Hence, clusters of flowers may in this way cross-fertilise among themselves even if no butterflies come to visit them.

The Red Valerian

Then the petal-tube and stamen fall from the seed-case pedestal, and the style, too, is carried with them, and only the urn-shaped ovary with its curious, ringed collar is left. The days pass, the fruits all ripen, and then the collar gives one a surprise, for it suddenly unrolls and forms a spreading ring of feathery rays which catch the wind, and in due course the little dry fruit is wafted away to some rocky niche. One single seed lies in it—one stamen, one style and stigma, one seed—the Red Valerian believes in economy of effort. Old Gerard is rather plaintive on the subject of the sailing seed; he tells us that "without great diligence the seed is not to be gathered or preserved, for my selfe have often endeavoured to see and yet have lost my labour." Parkinson, who thought the Red Valerian "very pleasant to behold," and gave it a place in his "Garden of Pleasant Flowers," also describes how "after these flowers have stood blowne a very great while, they sodainely fall away and the seed is ripe very quickly after, which is whitish standing upon

Wild Flowers as They Grow

the branches naked . . . with a little white downe at the end of every one of them, whereby they are soon carried away by the wind." The Red Valerian is noteworthy for flowering all through the summer months.

The leaves are of an unusually elegant shape. Rounded and broad at the base they taper to a fine point, and often are somewhat hollowed and boat-shaped. Thus they hold water for a certain length of time, whereas most plants construct their leaf-system so that water is conducted immediately to the roots. Perhaps this is a definite advantage to a plant that for choice lives on the top of a wall, or hangs from the side of a chalky cliff.

The name Valerian is said to come either from King Valerius, who dabbled in the healing art, or from the Latin *valere*—to heal. The family of this plant is the small one of the *Valerianeæ*, and its only relatives in the British flora are the Common Valerian, or " All Heal," the Pyrenean Valerian, and the four species of cornsalads.

THE PRIVET

LIGUSTRUM VULGARE

"THE Moon is lady of this," said the old herbalist - astrologers, and truly there is nothing hot or vivid about the Privet ; it is primness personified, with its neat, green leaves set two by

a, calyx. *b*, petals. *c*, stamens. *d*, stigma, style, ovary. *e*, berry.

two upon its stems, and its equally neat, trim pyramids of little flowers that top the branches in such orderly fashion. Primness and trimness rule, too, in all its details ; each leaf is a simple, narrow oval, with smooth, green surface, one main rib, and a plain, straight edge, and each flower is a regular

cross, and, of course, white, for gayness of garb
would seem as much out of place on the Privet as it
would on some precise, elderly spinster addicted to
black silk and white cap.

Even when the leaves first begin to appear, there
is no folding or rolling even of the most regular
description in the buds; each is born a very minute
object, and just grows bigger and bigger to full size.
One could imagine the horror of the Privet shrub—
if it could express itself—at such untidy folding as
that in the oak buds, or such crumpling as that in
the poppy buds. Then, again, the Privet always
wears its dress of seemly green, and this, in spite
of the fact, that it is not, strictly speaking, an
evergreen, since spring by spring the leaves
renew themselves. Yet its branches are never
revealed in their bare nakedness, for winter cannot
tear their vesture from them, and only when the
young leaves are ready to take their place do
the old leaves loose their hold and fall. Aurora
Leigh speaks of her little chamber being "as green

The Privet

as any privet hedge a bird might choose to build in."

It was this quality of continuous greenness, as well as its formality and its complaisance " to make hedges or arbours in gardens . . . wherein it is so apt that no other can be like unto it, to bee cut, lead and drawne into what form one will, either of beasts, birds, or men, armed or otherwise," that made it so acceptable in the gardens of our forefathers. Parkinson in the seventeenth century says that " the use of this plant is so much and so frequent throughout all this land . . . that I could not forget it "—that is, forget to place it among the plants in his " Earthly Paradise." Again, it was first favourite in those charming formal gardens of Queen Elizabeth's day when the walks were set between green hedges, to make which " every man taketh what liketh him best, as either privet alone, or sweet Bryar and Whitethorn interlaced together " ; and favourite, too, in days still earlier to fashion the " privy playing places " of the Middle Ages,

Wild Flowers as They Grow

such " a pleasaunt herber* well ywrought," as, for instance, Chaucer found :

> " And shapen was this herber, roofed all,
> As is a prety parlour ; and also
> The hegge† as thick as is a castle wall,
> That who that list withoute to stond or go,
> Though he would all day prien to and fro,
> He shoulde not see if there were any wighte
> Within or no. : : ."

As Parkinson suggests, the Privet takes it place with the yew, the box, and the holly as a topiary plant for the fashioning of those marvellous beasts without which no gentleman's garden was at one time complete, but upon which Alexander Pope poured such satire and so helped to kill the usage. We remember his " St. George in box ; his arm scarce long enough, but will be in a condition to stick the dragon by next April. A green dragon of the same with a tail of ground ivy for the present." It was not quite of the same rank, perhaps, as the box, and certainly not as the yew for this purpose,

* Arbour.   † Hedge.

The Privet

but it surpassed them in the rapidity of its growth, and hence the quickness with which it could be fashioned.

But not only have the leaves served in mass for screens and decorations, they were found of use individually by the old herbalists, who turned so much to account that we to-day think valueless. Thus a Dutchman in the time of King Henry VIII. was convinced that the leaves "made into powder are good to be strowed uppon hoale ulcers and naughtie festering," and, further, that "Whatsoever is burned or scalded with fire may be healed with the brothe of Privet leaves." In Belgium the clippings of the shrub are used in tanneries, as there is considerable astringency in the leaf tissues.

But the white flower pyramids have their points also as they stud the greenness in June and July days. A tiny green calyx cup supports the short tube of four united petals, which above turn back to form a precise cross. Above the petal-cross a pair of pale stamens peep. It is true that some-

Wild Flowers as They Grow

times the corolla may be five-lobed and the stamens three, just as the white cap of the aforementioned spinster *may* show irregularities, but, as is obvious from the comparison, it is an infrequent spectacle. An ovary appears below the petals and a short, clubbed column rises from it. At first the stamens stretch away from this column to give a chance for cross-fertilisation, later they bend over it to ensure self-fertilisation if necessary. Now, since primness never in any way necessarily spells lack of sweetness, we are not surprised to find that the cream pyramids are very sweet. A fragrance that somehow seems old-fashioned and redolent of the past wafts from them, and in the corolla tube a feast of honey is stored. Under sunshiny skies butterflies, bees, flies and beetles all come as eager visitors for what they can get, while in the dusk one moth is such a persistent visitor that it is named after the shrub the Privet Hawk moth, *Sphinx ligustri*, a handsome fellow, too, with grey wings and fluffy black and red body.

The Privet

The flowers persist for some time, then they begin to tinge with brown, and on the slightest movement crowds of the corollas fall to the ground —their tubes now much more readily seen. The ovaries swell and become a brighter, shinier green. Each has two chambers within it, and in each is a seed. Towards autumn they become black, and the dark clusters of fruit are very noticeable. The birds find them pleasant enough, and, indeed, the Germans express a mild oil from them which is used in cooking. A dye, too, which once served for tinting maps and such-like purposes, can be obtained from them.

The apparent primness of the plant has been emphasised here, but it is a remarkable thing that the old name of the plant, " Prim " or " Primprint," had nothing whatever to do with this quality. In the Middle Ages there appears to have been some extraordinary confusion between the names of this plant and that of the primrose, and on the principle that " a rose by any other name would smell as sweet," there seems to have been an interchange, which, according to Dr. Prior, came about thus : The primrose's Latin name was then *Ligustrum*, its common name " Prim," or " Primprint," from the French *prime printemps*, because it came so early in the spring. But on the continent *Ligustrum* was the Latin name given to the Privet, and in our first English herbal—that of Turner, dated about 1550 —*Ligustrum* was there retained as the generic name for the Privet. But since " Primprint " had always been its English equivalent that still went with it and was attached to the Privet too. " Primet " was an abbreviation of " Primprint " that had already served for the primrose, and it also was handed on and eventually softened into " Privet." It is rather an involved story altogether. Tusser, writing for gardeners in 1573, speaks of the Privet as " Prim," for among the work to be done in January he says :

"Now set ye may the box and bay,
Haithorne and prim for clothes trim."

94

The Privet

The Privet is usually a shrub about six to eight feet high, but sometimes it becomes almost a small tree if it be left alone and untrammelled. It is a member of the Olive family, the *Oleaceæ*, and its only other close relative native of this country is, strangely enough, the ash, though there is little or no family resemblance to be traced on the surface. To its foreign relatives, the lilacs, now almost naturalised here, there is a considerable likeness, though the Privet clusters are, of course, on a much smaller scale.

THE YELLOW CORYDALIS

CORYDALIS LUTEA

GREAT tufts of filmy leaves—curiously reminiscent of maidenhair and interspersed with clusters of pale yellow bird-like flowers—were decking the old red wall behind the herbaceous

a, sepals.   *b*, petals.   *c*, stamen in two groups.   *d*, ovary, style, stigma.
e, pod.

border. Long ago, no doubt, the Corydalis had been an invited guest into that garden, welcomed for the delicate charm of its colour and form, but, like other guests have been known to do, it had a little overstepped the limits of its welcome and a

96

The Yellow Corydalis

ruthless hand was tearing it out by the armful. It offered little opposition, for though it had "many crambling threddy roots," as an old writer said, and they were moreover, "somewhat thicke, grosse and fat," yet the crumbling mortar of the old wall gave it no encouragement to resist. It seemed hard on the plant, whose charms became even more insistent as one saw it more closely. Let us sum them up shortly.

The pale, wax-like stems are tinted with pink, and carry a curious suggestion of translucence about them, especially where they swell at the junction of leaf-stalk and main stem. The leaves are very many and closely intermingled in such a way that one keen observer described them as "confusedly placed" upon the stems. Part of this apparent confusion is due to their being very finely cut into many segments. Each is first divided into three main divisions, then each division is cut up into still finer divisions. On the top surface the colour is a subdued and delicate green, below it is still paler, and more delicate and subdued, so that when the wind rustles the leaves the green colouring of the foliage has a " shot " effect, as one says of a silk woven with strands of two colours.

Eight or nine, possibly even a dozen, flowers cluster together at the end of a stalk, but since the flowers all tend to turn in one direction—the direction of greatest light and that from which they may anticipate the advent of their visitors— the clusters have a one-sided appearance. They are particularly interesting, both for the elaborate plan on which they are designed and for the failure which so often attends their complex schemes. Each flower is set, as it were, across the end of its stalk—that is to say, the stalk appears to come from the side of the flower rather than from its end. It has only two little sepals, and the effect of these is entirely lost, since they are very minute and are coloured, moreover, very like the petals. The four petals form a closed box of peculiar shape. The top petal is much the largest ; in front

The Yellow Corydalis

it turns upwards and forms a kind of portico ; at the opposite end it curls over beyond the stalk in a thick, hollow spur. The two lateral petals are alike and smaller, and form the sides of the box. Towards the front each carries a little flap on its outer side. The lowest petal, which forms the floor of the box, is very interesting—the diagram shows its construction. Along its length runs a trench, open near the petal's base, then closing over, and widening out at the tip into a definitely marked depression—it is rather suggestive, in fact, of a pipe running into a pool.

The six stamens are collected into two groups, each group having a single broad filament with three minute branches at top, each branch carrying an anther. The pollen grains contained in the anthers are remarkable in that many different crystalline forms are found side by side in the same anther. Honey collects in the round, thick spur of the top petal, being exuded from a projection of the upper filament into the spur. The lowest petal might well be constructed for conducting the honey into the pool at its tip with a view to offering a " taster " to visitors, but there is no proof that this happens. The dark green seed-case is hidden in the petal box, and a long, transparent-looking filament carries the yellow stigma. Stamen-groups and ovary, style and stigma are completely enclosed in the box formed by the four petals. Kerner calls attention to the point " that Corydalis is almost unique amongst flowers in that it is lop-sided, i.e. the spurred petal is not in the median plane of the flower (as in the generality of zygo-morphic flowers), but is inserted laterally."

Now, apparently what the plant designs should happen is this : a big humble-bee approaches the flower " face on " and straddles across the side petals under the portico. The two flaps, already mentioned as on the smaller side petals, serve like stirrups to steady it and give it the purchase necessary for it to thrust its head with determination into the box, which is opening under its weight.

The Yellow Corydalis

As it inserts its proboscis into the spur a curious lever mechanism, forcing out stamens and stigma, scatters the pollen from the stamens upon its abdomen. It then withdraws its head and flies away. But the truth is that, after all this elaboration of plan, insects seem to care little about the Corydalis, and the plant's visiting list is a very short one. Indeed, it does not treat its visitors well; it is rather like the case in Æsop's Fables of the stork inviting the fox to a meal. The petal box of the flower is very long, the honey in the spur only reaches up a little way; therefore, when a hive bee settles upon the flower and goes to the trouble of pressing it open and attempting to partake of the honey provided, it finds its proboscis is too short to reach the desired nectar. Therefore, it must needs depart unsatisfied, its labour wasted. A humble-bee, whose proboscis is longer, fares a little better; it can, perhaps, just touch the honey, but it cannot sip it with ease; therefore it, too, goes away dissatisfied, and in neither case is there any encouragement to continue visiting other flowers of the Corydalis kind. This is particularly bad policy on the part of the plant, because it has so arranged its affairs that no flower can be fertilised by the pollen from its own stamens ; the ovules are absolutely irresponsive if the pollen grains that fall upon the stigma are from the anthers adjacent to it ; even if the pollen comes from other flowers on the same plant there seems little result ; it has, therefore, made itself absolutely dependent upon the kind offices of bees to convey the pollen from one plant to another. But the bees, wholly deluded if of the smaller hive kind, unsatisfied if of the larger "humble" sort, are not going to be altogether deprived of their anticipated feast, and so we find them turning burglars and biting through the tube from outside, and thrusting their probosces through the opening directly into the honey pool. Dishonesty pays in their case, they sup their fill ; the flower is punished for its maladroit arrangement, it loses its honey and no service is performed in return. It is, therefore, not surprising that it often fails to set seed. When it does succeed, it bears small, narrow pods containing several seeds, which pods open by two valves.

There are two Corydals which are now found growing wild in Great Britain : firstly, the Yellow Corydalis of our picture and description, known sometimes as the " Yellow Fumitory," and also " Mother of Thousands," from the very many little yellow flowers it bears ; secondly, the Climbing Corydal, which has small white flowers and climbs by means of its leaf-stalks, which possess delicate tendrils. But neither species is a true native of this country ; the Yellow Corydal comes from Barbary and southern Europe, the Climbing Corydal is native rather of western Europe. Both species blossom in June and July, and prefer stony places, the Yellow Corydal in particular is very much at home on old garden walls. Its family is that of the *Fumariaceæ*, and its nearest British relative the Fumitory.

THE DWARF THISTLE

CARDUUS ACAULIS

THERE was no mistaking it. Thistles of all sorts there were in plenty around : Musk Thistles, a couple of feet high with great, lovely, drooping

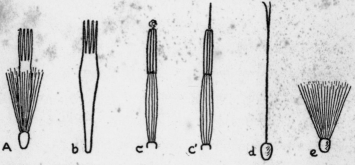

A, a floret showing ovary, calyx, corolla.   *b*, corolla.   *c*, stamens.
   c′, stamen, style protruding.   *d*, stigmas, style, ovary.   *e*, fruit.

heads of rich purple, formed a striking group ; Creeping Thistles, apparently belying their name, stood still higher, and showed ominous teeth round their single-sexed flower-heads, the males round, the

The Dwarf Thistle

females more oval; Carline Thistles, rivalling the Creeping Thistle in prickliness, were unique with their yellow shining rays—but the Dwarf Thistle, little as it was, held its own and caught the eye on those chalky, spreading Downs. Like so many small islands dotted about over the green sea of the close turf, its rosettes of leaves lay, each like a many-rayed star, close pressed to the earth, each ray a single leaf radiating from one central point, the point where the thick root entered the ground. The ray-like character was emphasised by the pale midrib which ran down the centre of each leaf, while the design was elaborated and decorated by the fact that the margin of the leaves was cut into great teeth right down to the aforesaid midrib, each of these teeth being itself jagged and toothed again, and every ultimate green tooth ending in a sharp, colourless spine. "Surely Mars rules it, it is such a prickly business," one echoed Culpepper as one looked down on the plant; but nevertheless there was great beauty of design in every one of those thistle-leaf islands when one came to consider them.

In the centre of each of the rosettes a number of buds and flowers in all stages stood erect on the shortest of stalks, and formed a brilliant red-purple centre to the green star. The earliest stage was represented by a flower-head bud rather like a green, cupless acorn, with an outer coat of many over-lapping scales ; an older stage had a flat, white top faintly tinged with purple because the coat had opened and disclosed the light tips of a multitude of feathery hairs and lilac tubes, all tightly pressed together and held in place by the aforesaid coat. A still later stage showed at one point a little ear where several of the purple tubes had suddenly shot up beyond the others, and so in successive stages the number of these rapidly increased until the full-blown Thistle was presented.

If one had rooted up one of these Dwarf Thistles —and the deed is not to be cavilled at, for in spite of their attractiveness they are all pests that take up

The Dwarf Thistle

space and kill the turf beneath—and with a sharp knife had slit right down through the flowering Thistle-brush, this is what one would have found, turning it round and about : firstly, that the coat of green, overlapping scales had no sharp points, and so the head could be handled with pleasure, which is more than can be said of many of the Thistle-heads ; secondly, that some eighty to a hundred long, slender florets were set on a hard receptacle or platform. If one or two had been isolated and laid side by side, one would have discovered a little cream-coloured ovary at the base of each, and on it a ring of many silky white hairs, three quarters of an inch long, maybe, standing round a gleaming white tube no thicker than a pin. Above the hairs, however, the tube had swelled a little and also become a red-purple, its top being fringed into fine, erect segments. Honey lay invitingly in the depths. Inside the tube, fine though it was, was a still finer one formed by the heads of the five stamens, and through this, in due time, pushed, like a piston, a red-purple rod clothed with hairs, thrusting before it white pollen grains. In some of the florets the silvery ball of pollen could have been seen lying just on the top of the anther tube—the anthers, by the way, having opened on the inside and discharged their contents into the tube. Matters had been carried a stage farther in florets on the outer ring of these, for the style-piston had grown and thrust the pollen ball off its perch on to the adjacent florets, or, perhaps, the ball had been removed by the body and legs of those many bees and flies that specially favour Thistle flowers, and in their visits smear the pollen from one floret to another, or carry it bodily from one head to another. As the style was completing its growth the stamen filaments contracted, and so the anther cylinder was drawn back into the corolla, thus the stylar column was left bare beyond the petal tube. It then forked into two branches roughened with papillæ, and these stretched out waiting for pollination. Later they curved over and touched the sweeping hairs, and

The Dwarf Thistle

thus might have been self-fertilised by any pollen grains still clinging to them.

If we had then turned from our dissected head to its whole neighbour we should have seen how the florets wither and the petal tubes fall away, though the little one-seeded ovaries with their crown of silver hairs still retain their hold on the hard receptacle within the enfolding green bracts. But in still older flower-heads we should have discovered how at length even their hold slackens and their silvery hairs spread a little and assert their true rôle of parachute ; on older heads in the sunshine the fruits would be making their escape, asking but the merest movement of the air to carry their feather-weights—

" Thistle beard
That skimmed the surface of the dead calm lake,
Suddenly halting now—a lifeless stand !
And starting off again with freak as sudden,
In all its sportive wanderings, all the while
Making report of an invisible breeze
That was its wings, its chariot, and its horse,
Its playmate, rather say, its moving soul."

(*Wordsworth*.)

Wild Flowers as They Grow

But it is not to be imagined that the Thistle-down so often seen floating is necessarily carrying its seed burden, for more likely than not it is a parachute that has lost its passenger. So lightly attached is the seed that a little jar against a branch, a leaf, or what not, or even an extra gust of wind, will detach it, leaving the feathery hairs to sail on, though their work is accomplished. It must be noticed that these hairs are each feathery, a point of apparently little moment, but one on which the botanist lays stress as a basis for classification, those Thistles with a "feathery pappus" being said to be in the group *Cnicus*, those with simple pappus (plain hairs) being *Carduus* proper.

The Dwarf Thistle is essentially a plant of chalky downs and open heaths. Its flowers are found in July, August, and September, and, with all the other eleven kinds of Thistles that plague our farmers, it is classed in the great family of the *Compositæ*. Its root is particularly thick and woody, and was at one time chewed as a remedy for toothache.

THE WILD THYME

THYMUS SERPYLLUM

" AND because the breath of flowers is far
sweeter in the air (where it comes and
goes, like the warbling of music) than in the hand,
therefore nothing is more fit for that delight than

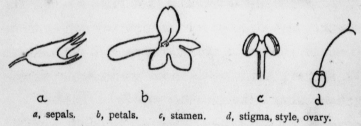

a b c d

a, sepals. *b*, petals. *c*, stamen. *d*, stigma, style, ovary.

to know what be the flowers and plants that do best
perfume the air," and then Lord Bacon, planning
his " princely garden," gives an annotated list of
fragrant flowers, adding, " but those which perfume
the air most delightfully, not passed by as the rest,
but being trodden upon and crushed, are three ;

that is burnet, wild thyme, and watermints ; therefore, you are to set whole alleys of them, to have pleasure when you walk or tread." *His* garden was not to appeal to the eye alone !

Wild Thyme has always been taken as the emblem of fragrance and sweetness. Its very name Thyme (in Greek form) was first given it by the Greeks as a derivative from a word which meant " to fumigate," either because they used it as their incense, or because it was taken as a type of all such sweet-smelling herbs. Strangely enough this little plant, so deeply rooted in the affections and thoughts of Englishmen, has never been known by any common native name, though occasionally " Thyme " is qualified in some way, such as Running Thyme, Wild Thyme, or Mother of Thyme. (An odd synonym or two, such as " Brother Wort," " Hill Wort," or " Pella Mountain," are purely local terms.) Also, though the plant is so abundant and familiar in Great Britain to-day, we never find it mentioned in old English vocabularies ; apparently

The Wild Thyme

the first reference to it is in a " Pictorial Vocabulary " of 1440. A question has therefore been raised as to whether it is a true native, but, anyway, by Spenser's and Shakespeare's day it was certainly fully at home. The former speaks of the " bees-alluring time," while everyone is familiar with the latter's description of the bower of the Queen of the Fairies, the " bank where the wild thyme blows."

Perhaps the reason why Thyme became peculiarly the emblem of sweetness is that Mount Hymettus, near Athens, was covered with Wild Thyme, and there the bees buzzed unceasingly, and there they gathered honey of special flavour and sweetness, so in the minds and writings of the ancients sweetness and Thyme were inextricably united. " Thyme for the time it lasteth, yieldeth most and best honni, and therefore in old time was accounted chief," said an old English writer.

Wild Thyme is really a tiny shrub—indeed, one of the smallest—with little hard, many-branched twigs that look smooth but are, all the same, covered with minute hairs all pointing down from the flowers, as any creeping insect may discover. There are hairs, too, few but long, on the base of the leaves and on the sepals of the flowers. Perhaps they are to keep guard over the honey-filled flowers, but more probably they are a coat which shields the plant somewhat from the sun's heat, and helps it to retain its moisture, for, as Alphonse Karr reminds us, " If there is an arid, stony, dry soil burnt up by the sun, it is there thyme spreads its charming green beds, perfumed, close, thick, elastic."

The little plain, oval leaves lie along the stem in pairs, but they very readily fall from the stalks. " The floures grow about the toppe of the stalkes like to crownes or garlands," wrote Lyte in Queen Elizabeth's day, and these clusters of perhaps forty or fifty flowers are dark in colour, relieved by touches of a paler lilac. The darkness is due to the massed calyces of the various flowers, for these are a purplish green. Each is two-lipped, the upper projecting lip having three teeth, the lower lip two sharp teeth.

The Wild Thyme

White hairs fringe it, particularly on the outer sides of the lower lip. Out of the calyx a lilac, two-lipped, tubular corolla projects, its white tube lying easily within the calyx like a long neck in a loose collar. This corolla reverses the form of the calyx, for the upper lip with two lobes is the shorter, while the lower lip with three is large and spreading. But after we have got so far in our investigation differences in the flowers meet us both on the same plant and in flowers on different plants. For instance, in the youngest and freshest flowers on a certain plant four stamens are projecting far beyond the petals, the halves of the anthers being very distinct, for they are set, a little apart, on the ends of their filaments. Each half is slitting down its length and pollen is escaping. In a somewhat older flower there are only the remains of four withered stamens to be seen, but, instead, there is a forked column thrust straight out like the traditional forked tongue of a dragon. It is trying to catch some of the pollen from those younger and fresher

flowers that is being carried about by bees. Therefore, each of the flowers on this particular plant is,
to all intents and purposes, male at the beginning
of its life, and female in the latter part.

But if we turn to other plants whose flowers
are perhaps a trifle lighter in colour and a little
smaller, we shall look in vain for the first male stage,
or for any remnants of withering stamens, for in them
there is only a projecting, dragon-tongued stigma,
with the long style running back to the four nutlets
at the base. These are exclusively female flowers.
Some botanists say they have also found male flowers
i.e. flowers which have stamens only—particularly
in Italy—but it is very doubtful if there are any
such in England. Here only the hermaphrodite
flowers (i.e. the flowers with both sets of organs)
and the female flowers are known, and the two
are about equally distributed. With this provision
for promoting cross-fertilisation the plant is content.
It is asserted that it has absolutely no power of
self-fertilisation.

The Wild Thyme

After the lilac corollas fall off certain hairs inside the calyx stretch out and form a shining, rayed disk covering over the four nutlets that lie at the base. This disk makes a gleaming white spot noticeable within every calyx in which the maturing of the seeds is progressing. It serves, perhaps, to hide them from small animals which might otherwise make their dinner off them.

The fragrance of the leaves of the Thyme is due to an essential oil that permeates their tissues : a variety of the same oil in a stronger form gives our Garden Thyme (*Thymus vulgaris*) its flavouring value for such culinary purposes as " stuffing " for poultry. This species of Thyme is a native of Southern Europe where, indeed, especially in the Mediterranean district, the Thymes grow in full force. The plant serves as a badge of extreme Republicanism in the South of France.

The herbalists of old found many uses for our little Wild Thyme. " Running Thyme mengled with Vinegar and oyle of Roses and applied to the forehead

swageth headache and is very good against raving
and frenzie." Also, "the perfume of the same
driveth away all venemous beasts," and so forth.
Thyme, too, is specially associated with death ; it
is one of the fragrant plants that are favoured for
planting on graves—in Wales particularly none but
sweet-scented plants are tolerated for this purpose.
The Oddfellows carry sprigs of Thyme at funerals
and throw them into the grave of their dead brother.
Superstition asserts that to carry a sprig of Wild
Thyme into a house brings the direst ill-luck to the
family ; should death or serious illness follow in
the immediate future, the blame is all cast on the
unfortunate bearer of the twig. An old tradition
says that Thyme was one of the herbs that formed
the fragrant bed of the Virgin Mary. The Thyme,
too, is one of the fairies' flowers, and tufts of Thyme
are one of their favourite playing grounds. Anyone
who doubts this statement must stand on Midsummer
night under an elder bush, near where Wild Thyme
is growing and watch for the fairies himself !

THE COMMON MALLOW

MALVA SYLVESTRIS

FROM the very beginning of its existence the Mallow possesses points of special interest. As an embryo it lies curled round in a kidney-shaped seed, its root enfolded by the base of its two seed-

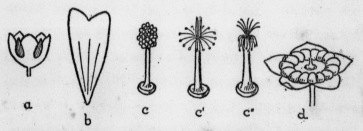

a, calyx and epicalyx. *b*, petal. *c, c', c''*, successive positions of stamens and stigmas. *d*, fruit on calyx.

leaves. It almost fills the seed, but a little reserve food is stored away with it. When it creeps out of its temporary home its seed-leaves prove to be of an unusual character, for whereas the majority of such leaves have a plain, unbroken outline, those of the Mallow are three-lobed. This cutting into lobes has been brought about by the peculiar manner in which the leaves are folded within the seed coat.

During its first summer season the little plant merely establishes itself and forms root, stem, and leaves, but the following spring sees it at the top of its vigour; its growth pushes on apace, and it races upwards two, or even three, feet. Its stems —it mostly boasts of several rising from the root— are covered with stiff hairs, as are the leaf-stalks. Its leaves are large and rounded, and cut into five or seven shallow lobes. The margin is still further diversified by a small nicking. Our ancestors had a great opinion of these leaves, though nowadays we seem to overlook any possibility of merit in them. Once they were quite a common vegetable. They were also used as a " sallet " with salt and vinegar. In the herbalists' medical lore they took an important place; rubbed on spots stung by wasps and bees, they quickly eased the pain; they also drew forth

The Common Mallow

thorns and splinters if applied to the wounds where these had entered. In an old book of the seventeenth century, " The Art of Simpling," it is said, " Mallowes, Pellitory, and Mercury are reckoned weeds by the Vulgar, and yet they are 3 of the 5 emollient herbes which are used in every glister." In fact, the whole plant from root to fruit is full of a mucilaginous sap, and it is from this that it acquired its reputation both as food and as a medicine. We can understand, therefore, how decoctions of the plant were prescribed for coughs, sore throats, and inflammations generally. Further, " If the head be washed therewith it stays the falling and shedding of the hair," says Culpepper in his account of the plant. He ends with a little piece of interesting biography. Once during those Elizabethan days an epidemic of a serious and mysterious nature occurred. " The College of Physicians not knowing what to make of it called it the inside plague for their wits were *Ne plus ultra* about it. . . ." His son was taken ill, " myself being in the country was sent for up ;

the only thing I gave him was Mallows bruised and boiled both in milk and drink, in 2 days (the blessing of God being upon it) it cured him. And I here, to shew my thankfulness to God, in communicating it to his creatures, leave it to posterity."

In June the clusters of many green buds begin to be pink-tipped as rose-red cones gradually project beyond their green envelopes. One says " envelopes " advisedly, for the Mallow flower is not content with a calyx only, even though it is stout and hairy, it must needs also provide an outer, extra wrap of three small, green bracts which are inserted on the five-lobed calyx cup. In one respect these little bracts are important, for on their various peculiarities is based the three divisions of the whole Mallow family—the *Malvaceæ*—as represented in England, namely (1) *Malva*—the Mallows proper, of which there are three, the Common, the Musk, and the Dwarf Mallow, where the bracts are separate and on the calyx ; (2) *Lavertera*—the Tree Mallow— where the bracts are joined into a three-lobed cup ;

122

The Common Mallow

(3) *Althæa*—the Marsh Mallow (to which group the garden hollyhock belongs), where the bracts are united into a five-lobed cup. Each cone bursts and spreads as five distinct petals, which together form a wide vase. Every petal is narrow where it is attached, but spreads at the top, where the centre of its margin is notched; it is also scored by deep, red-purple lines—honey guides—from flower-centre to margin.

Looking down on one of these flowers one sees a rose-purple disk with five lobes, and in its centre a five-rayed, green star, which star is due to the green of the calyx showing through the five gaps between the lower parts of the petals. But the most striking feature of the Mallow flower is its central arrangement. Rising from a white platform, on which honey glistens, is an elegant column, slightly spreading at the base and ornamented with purple panels. At the top of the column is a fluffy, pyramid-like head. The column is the united stamen filaments; the fluffy head the many branches of the stamens with their single white anthers. At the outset the pyramid of anthers completely covers over the as yet undeveloped stigmas, but as the anthers open and let fall their pollen, they droop one by one until eventually they have all fallen away and hang limply round the column. And as they fall we see that there are many thin ovary columns within—many styles each with a receptive stigma. These grow and speedily occupy precisely the position that the stamens did.

Hosts of insects visit the Mallow plants—Müller counted no fewer than fifty different sorts that do so—and these will rub indiscriminately on either stamens or stigmas according as they visit a younger or an older flower, and thus necessarily will transfer the pollen from the one to the other. Most of the visitors are after the flower's honey, which is produced in pockets at the base of the ovary and covered over by hairs to keep rain from diluting it and little, unprofitable insects from stealing it, but there are others who come for the sake of the abundant pollen. In the Dwarf Mallow, where the

The Common Mallow

flowers are smaller and insect visitors far fewer, the styles eventually curl down among the withering stamens, and thus fertilise themselves if this has not already been done by the kind offices of insects.

Every country child knows the fruit of the Mallow, those little so-called "cheeses" (because they resemble a flattened, round Dutch cheese), made up, like a peeled Tangerine orange, of a dozen or more segments, each segment being a cell of the ovary and containing a single, curved seed. "Only compare a vegetable cheese," says one, "with all that is exquisite in marking and beautiful in arrangement in the works of man, and how poor and contemptible do the latter appear! Nor is it alone externally that this inimitable beauty is to be discovered. Cut the cheese across and every slice brings to view cells and partitions and seeds and embryos arranged with an unvarying regularity which would be past belief if we did not know from experience how far beyond all that the mind can conceive is the symmetry with which the works of Nature are constructed."

Wild Flowers as They Grow

As the cheese dries the segments fall apart, and in the new spring each will, under favourable auspices, develop into a new plant to carry on the life-sequence —for its parent having lived its two seasons' life, is by then dead. And thus we complete the cycle of the Mallow's life.

Many favourite, homely names for the plant are taken from the fruits : thus we have " Cheese-cake," " Cheese-flower," " Chucky Cheese," " Loaves of Bread," " Pancake Plant," " Pick Cheese," and " Fairy Cheese."

The name Mallow is supposed to be derived from a Greek word meaning " to soften," either because of its laxative qualities or because of qualities in its mucilaginous tissues already alluded to. Gerard, however, derives it from a Hebrew word signifying " of the saltness," " because the Mallow groweth in saltish and old ruinous places, . . . which in most abundant manner yieldeth forth Salt peter and such-like matter."

THE GREAT MULLEIN

VERBASCUM THAPSUS

" HEDGE taper," " High taper," " Hig taper,"
" Hag taper," " Our Lady's Candle "—
the names of the country-side all give the keynote
to the Mullein's character—" the whole top with his

a   b   bc   c   d

a, sepals.   *b*, petals.   *bc*, stamen on petal.   *c*, stamens.
d, stigma, style, ovary.

pleasant yellow floures sheweth like to a wax candle
or taper cunningly wrought "—and on the lane
borders, among the dark nettles and woundworts,
the pale spikes light up wonderfully the still darker
hedgeside in late summer days. All the first four
synonyms are derived from the Anglo-Saxon *hege*,

or *haga*, a hedge, and "Hig" and "Hag" have really nothing to do with witches in spite of the popular idea (obtained from the name-corruption) that the Mullein was the witches' taper. No doubt the name "Taper" was largely due to the resemblance mentioned by Lyte as above, but it has a double appropriateness for, as Parkinson tells us, "Verbascum is called of the Latines Candela regia and Candelaria, because the elder age used the stalks dipped in suet to burne, whether at funeralls or otherwise," and Gerard, in his "Grete Herball," also remarks that it is "a plant whereof is made a maner of lynke (link), if it be talowed." "Our Lady's Candle," or now "Lady's Candle," recalls the fact that in the days from which this name has been handed down to us every church had its candles burning in front of the shrine of the Madonna. (But if the Great Mullein suggests a single, tall candle, in what a magnificent and elaborate way does that other wild but far rarer Mullein—the Hoary Mullein (*Verbascum pulverulentum*)—carry

The Great Mullein

out the candlestick suggestion ? On chalk or sand, in Norfolk or Suffolk, one may find it as tall as oneself, a candelabrum of many branches, branches frosted with thick, silvery hairs, each branch tipped with pale yellow flowers, the whole a model of such stately symmetry and beauty that it stands unrivalled in our whole British flora.)

In the Great Mullein a solitary, stiff, pale stem rises from a rosette of thick, flannel-like leaves ; its fibres are tough and strong and enclose a thin rod of white pith. Its rigid uprightness accounts for the plant's names of " Jupiter's " or " Jacob's Staff," " Aaron's Rod," and " Shepherd's Club." All the way up it is hugged by stalkless, thick, woolly leaves, leaves which indeed have their mid-rib from a quarter to half-way up the blade actually joined to the stem.

Their woolliness is caused by the whole leaf, back and fore, being covered with white hairs ; under a lens one can see that each hair is branched, " reminding one of tiny fir trees," and this, of course, makes for thickness of felting. They are very easily detachable and, in fact, in the Hoary Mullein they often lie almost like meal upon the leaf surface. In several ways they are of great use to the plant. They are a protective coat, checking too great a giving off of the plant's moisture ; conversely, too, they will not "wet"—rain and dew run off them— and thus the water pores, or stomata, lying in the epidermis beneath them, are left unclogged and can perform their due measure of transpiration, or giving off of watery vapour. Further, they are a definite weapon of defence, for they set up an intense irritation in the mucous membrane of any grazing animals that may attempt to browse upon them, and hence the plants are usually left severely alone by them. Those folks addicted to Mullein tea—and it is a homely remedy of the greatest antiquity for coughs and colds—well know how necessary it is to strain through fine muslin the hot water that has been poured over the flowers, so as to remove any hairs that may be floating in it. If not removed

The Great Mullein

one pays the penalty with an intolerable itching of the mouth. This woolliness of the leaves is responsible for still other synonyms for the plant, such as " Old Man's Flannel," " Adam's Flannel," " Our Lady's Flannel," " Beggar's Blanket," " Hare's Beard," and " Fluffweed."

Towards the top of the stalk the much-diminished leaves merge into the dense flower-spike. The flowers, too, are stalkless, and each is enclosed in a woolly calyx deeply cut into five lobes. The corolla, a somewhat irregular cup, is formed of five petals which are free above as five rounded lobes, but united at the base to form a very short tube. Their golden colour led to their being used to make a hair-wash for those fair ladies who desired golden locks ; thus Lyte tells us, " The golden floures of Mulleyn stiped in lye, causeth the heare to war yellow being washed therewithall." The stamens stand on the corolla ; there are five of them, three shorter than the other two, and these three have a large number of tiny hairs on the upper part of their filaments. It is supposed that these hairs, turgid and full of sap, are offered as delicate baits to the insect world, and supplement in this fashion the allurement of the honey that lies round the base of the ovary. These three stamens have only short, one-celled anthers; the two longer stamens have larger anthers. As the anthers open they disclose an orange-red inner surface. The ovary is rounded and hairy; hairs, too, appear on the lower part of the style, though the upper part is smooth; the stigma is slightly bifid.

Since the flowers are vertical the larger side of the petal-cup forms a platform for insects to alight on, while all five stamens are above the style. All kinds of insects are attracted by this plant, flies as well as bees, since the honey and the staminal hairs are both so readily accessible. The stigma is mature before the anthers have opened their red-lined pollen-sacs, and the style projects at the moment the flower opens, so that any kind of insect approaching it must needs strike it before entering. Cross-fertili-

The Great Mullein

sation, therefore, seems practically inevitable in these early days of the flowers' short existence. When the anthers are beginning to open the style falls either downwards or sideways, so there is a clear passage to the newly discharged pollen. Probably part of it at least is now carried away by the visitors. Then, as the flower ages, the stigma is raised once more into its old place, the stamens curl over and press their anthers towards it ; the petals, too, close up and tend to bring the two together, and so there is opportunity given for self-fertilisation to remedy any miss in the scheme of cross-fertilisation. The seed-capsule is very hard, and contains many seeds, which eventually escape through two valves.

This Mullein is a biennial, so it takes two seasons to bring it to maturity. It belongs to that remarkable family, the *Scrophulariaceæ*, which embraces members so diverse as the foxglove and the speedwell, the Mullein and the toadflax, as well as that quaint series of semi-parasites, the eyebrights, the bartsias, and the louseworts. Six species of Mullein are found in this country, some with white flowers and some with yellow. The Great Mullein is easily distinguished from among them by the already-mentioned union of the leaf-surface with the flower-stalk. Its flowering period is in July and August.

As a curative agent the Mullein stood in the past in the front rank. A decoction of its roots was one of the thousand and one alleviations our ancestors attempted for toothache; a matutinal draught of the distilled water of the flowers was most excellent for gout; Mullein juice and powder made from the dried roots rubbed on rough warts quickly removed them, though one's labour was wasted if the warts were smooth; a poultice made of the seeds and leaves with hot wine "draw forth speedily thorns or splinters gotten into the flesh," and so on, practically *ad infinitum*. Even the lower creation was not forgotten in its remedial power, as its name, "Bullock's Lungwort," implies; and Coles, in 1757, remarks that "Husbandmen of Kent do give it

The Great Mullein

their cattle against the cough of the lungs," and
this pioneer of veterinary science adds, "And I,
therefore mention it because Cattle are also in some
sort to be provided for in their deseases." But
that virtue does really reside in the plant is shown
in that it has stood the test of these days of science,
and is still found taking its place in the British
Pharmacopœia.

As for the word Mullein itself, Dr. Prior finds
an interesting history for it. It was "Molegn" in
Anglo-Saxon days, and "Malen" in old French, derived from the Latin *malandrium*, i.e. the melanders
or leprosy: "The term 'malandre' became also
applied to diseases of cattle, to lung diseases among
the rest, and this plant being used as a remedy
acquired its names of 'Mullein' and 'Bullock's
Lungwort.'"

THE CORN-COCKLE

LYCHNIS GITHAGO

"Allons! Allons!—Sow'd cockle, reap'd no corn."

Love's Labour's Lost.

THE Corn-Cockle takes its place in the ranks of the corn. Its stiff, bare stems, covered

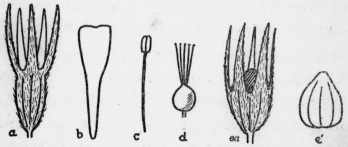

a, calyx. *b*, petal. *c*, stamen. *d*, styles, ovary. *ea*, fruit enclosed in calyx. *e'*, fruit isolated.

with close, rough hairs, merge with the corn-stalks, and it is only the little magenta islands of the flowers amid the corn-heads that catch the eye. In the attempt to break through the harsh stem

The Corn-Cockle

and gather the flowers the whole plant is apt to come up bodily, and then one can examine it at one's leisure—an ugly plant, barring its charming flowers, but with a certain strength and robust vitality about it that command one's respect.

Spring by spring it renews itself from seed— little rough seeds stored with a packet of reserve material round which the embryo curls like a horseshoe. The germinating plant quickly absorbs this reserve through its seed-leaves, and then withdraws them from the now otherwise empty husk. They are still very tender and the nights yet chilly, so though these twin leaves spread apart by day they draw together for mutual warmth at night.

By early July days it is amazing how much the plant has done ; its root is as thick as one's finger, and as hard as wood. A single stem rises from it. Two or three inches up are a pair of leaves—mean, narrow slips, several inches long and half an inch wide—with prominent midrib along their backs. (Broad-bladed leaves would be quite out of place and useless, too, amid the corn-stalks.) They have no stalks, and in the pocket that each forms with the main stem a branch arises. Each branch again gives off a pair of similar, though smaller, leaves, and again in their pockets a branch is formed; thus we have a plant continually forking, with a few ugly pairs of leaves which get more and more negligible.

On straight, very long stalks the flowers arise— the plant's one beauty. A peculiar spikiness, due to the fashioning of the sepals, is the outstanding feature of each. For the sepals, commencing as a cup, say half an inch high, covered with long, silky hairs all pointing upwards, and supported by ten strong ribs, are continued above the cup as five long, green spikes which stretch far beyond even the petal disk, and hence a country name for the plant is " Ray." Slit a flower down and examine it. On the inner side of the sepal cup are ten remarkable white ridges corresponding to the spaces between the ribs on the outer side. This well-

The Corn-Cockle

braced cup is essential to hold the petals together, for these have no power of supporting themselves, since the lower part, or limb, of each is of the thinnest and most fragile description, though above it spreads into a substantial enough looking object. Now look down on another flower and view it as it would appear to a hovering insect, and we see a five-rayed star with a large, five-lobed, purple disk shading in the centre to white ; on the disk are mysterious lines pointing down to a deep, green tunnel, from whose depths rises in the very centre a purple spot, the clustered tops of five columns. The slit flower shows that round the walls of the petal-tunnel stand ten stamens, while at the base is the ball-like ovary, from whose top rise the five clustered style-columns round which is gathered honey.

The structure bespeaks a member of the *Caryo-phylaceæ* family—the campions and the pinks—and hence the plant is often known as the " Corn-Campion," or the " Corn-Pink," and, indeed, its nearest relatives are the white campion and the ragged robin. The length of its long tube, and the distance of the honey from the mouth of the flower, indicate that it is essentially a butterfly and moth flower: no other insects have probosces long enough to reach down so deep a pit. When the flower opens, five of the stamens—those opposite the sepals—have their anthers discharging their pollen, though in the centre of the flower the five styles, taller than the stamens, are still in a tight bundle. For a day, at least, the flower remains thus, and visiting butterflies and bees carry off this pollen. Then the anthers drop from these five stamens, but the styles open out in the centre and with, literally, " open arms " receive visitors for what they can get. Meanwhile, the other five stamens are maturing, and their filaments growing, so that a little later, when their anthers open, they are on a par with the stigmas, and their contents are poured out over them. Thus cross-fertilisation is first planned, and self-fertilisation is the second string to the bow.

During the few days of the plant's life the petals

The Corn-Cockle

close protectingly at night, but one morning they do not re-open, but wither and fall. The ovary swells until it is the size and form of a small acorn, and always it is surrounded by the hairy sepal cup, and guarded by the five great, green points. The swelling causes the ten ribs of the calyx cup to depart from their parallelism, and to form a pattern like a Gothic window. If the handsome fruit be dissected when it is young it proves to consist of a green case closely fitting over a cone, which cone of immature seeds looks as though it had been cut jig-saw-wise into segments, and the segments left *in situ*. In these early days the cone lies in a bath of sweet mucilage, and each white seed tastes like an immature grain of corn. Later the mucilage is absorbed, the segments turn black, the cone falls to pieces, and in the dried case the ripe seeds rattle, and by the swaying of the wind are jerked out through five valves that open at its summit. Each seed has a roughened surface, and has been compared to a miniature, rolled-up hedgehog.

Wild Flowers as They Grow

This plant is commonly said to be "a weed of cultivation," that is, a weed not really indigenous, but introduced at some period or other, in this case probably with corn. On the other hand, Professor Earle argues that since the Saxon form of its name is *Coccel*, and that word is not found in kindred dialects, it may be of Celtic origin and link the plant with the beginnings of our country's story. But this is no real argument, for the word "cockle" was at one time used in a general sense for "weed." In a "Herbal to the Bible," issued in 1585, we are expressly told "under the name Cockle and Darnel is comprehended all vicious, noisome and unprofitable graine, encombring and hindering good corne." Spenser says :

> "And thus of all my harvest-hope I have
>   Nought reaped but a weedie crop of care,
> Which, when I thought have thresht a swelling sheave
>   Cockle for corn and chaff for barley bare."

And when Job said, "Let thistles grow instead of wheat, and cockle instead of barley," the sense was

The Corn-Cockle

general, as is shown by the alternative reading given in the margin, " or, noisome weed " ; and so, too, when Latimer exclaimed with fervour from the pulpit, " Oh that our prelates would bee as diligent to sowe the corne of goode doctrine as Sathan is to sowe Cockle and Darnel." But in the sixteenth century its application began to be narrowed down, and in the 1623 edition of Gerard this description accompanies a picture of the plant in question : " Cockle is a common and hurtfull weed in our Corne, and very well knowne by the name of Cockle . . . What hurt it doth among corne, the spoile of bread, as well in colour, taste and unwholesomenesse, is better known than desired."

For its specific name *Githago*—" this floure is now called among the learned githago," wrote Dodonæus in 1583—and its old English name *Gith*, it is difficult to find a meaning. " Pawple " and " Papple," of course, refer to the purple colour, while " Cockweed " is a slurring for " Cockleweed."

THE SELF-HEAL

PRUNELLA VULGARIS

SAID old Cole, in the reign of Charles II.,
" It " (i.e. the Self-heal) " is called by
modern writers (for neither the ancient Greek nor
Latin writers knew it) Brunella from Brunellen, which

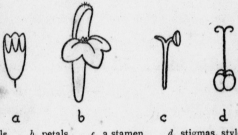

a, sepals.　　*b*, petals.　　*c*, a stamen.　　*d*, stigmas, style, ovary.

is a name given unto it by the Germans because it
cureth that inflamation of the mouth which they
call ' die Breuen,' yet the generall name of it in
Latine now-a-days is Prunella, as being a word of a
more gentile Pronunciation." And since we are

144

The Self-Heal

nothing if not " genteel " to-day, it is still, and chiefly, Prunella with us. This quotation disposes at once of the common belief that it was Linnæus who softened down the harsh *Brunella* for euphony's sake, since the " Father of modern botany " lived a century later than the writer of " Adam in Eden." As to the disease referred to, " it is common to soldiers when they lye in camp, but especially in garrisons, coming with an extraordinary inflammation or swelling as well in the Mouth as Throat," Cole further explains ; and then he destroys our faith in the plant's efficacy by giving as his reason for his belief in it as a remedy, " the very signature of the Throat which the form of the Flowers do represent signifying as much." For there once more we are confronted with the worthless old heresy —the Doctrine of Signatures. We now know that plants have not been labelled in some subtle way as to the benefits they are able to confer upon ailing humanity.

But the implicit faith of our forefathers in it,

as is exemplified in its names—Self-heal, " All-heal," " Hook-heal," " Slough-heal "—was probably rooted in some measure of fact all the same ; the old herbalists were so explicit on the point and appealed so confidently to experience. " There is not a better Wound herbe in the world than that of Self-heale is, the very name importing it to be very admirable upon this account, and indeed the Vertues doe make it good, for this very herbe without the mixture of any other ingredient being onely bruised and wrought with the point of a knife upon a Trencher, or the like, will be brought into the forme of a Salve, which will heal any green Wounde even in the first intention . . . after a very wonderfull manner," is one testimony ; while another, made a hundred years previously, speaks similarly of " Prunell," then immediately adds, with a fine disregard of uniformity in spelling, " Prunel brused with oile of roses and vinegar, and laid to the fore-part of the head, swageth and helpeth the pain and aking thereof," and sums up, " To be short, it serveth

The Self-Heal

for the same that Bugle doth, and in the world there are not two better wound herbs as hath bin often proved." (The virtues of the bugle have already been set forth in Vol. II. of this series.)

This wonderful herb is one of the great *Labiatæ* —the two-lipped—clan, but happily it has a quite distinctive personality, which is by no means always the case in that perplexing family. It may at once be known because on the top of its flowering stalks the flowers are " thicke set together like an eare or spiky knap," i.e. an ear of corn. No other plant is at all like it. Immediately below this ear are a pair of stalkless leaves standing out on either side like a collar.

The flowers and bracts of this " ear " are arranged in most regular tiers; each tier is composed of a ring of six stalkless flowers, supported by a couple of spreading, green bracts. The number of tiers varies; there may be a dozen, there may be only half a dozen. Each flower consists of a two-lipped calyx, the upper lip very wide and flat, edged with three blunt teeth, the lower lip much narrower and with two long, pointed teeth. Both lips have red margins and carry hairs. Out of this somewhat uncommon calyx the petals project as an aggressive-looking, two-lipped corolla, of a deep purple hue. The upper lip is strongly arched, and on the top of the arch many hairs stand on end. The lower lip, of much the same length, spreads out into three lobes. Both lips join farther back into a tube which fits into the calyx as scissors in a sheath. Under the roofing upper lip are two pairs of stamens, one pair longer than the other, but both of remarkable structure. Instead of the anthers being set straight on the top of their filaments as is usual, each filament ends in two little branches, one of which carries an anther, the other—the one towards the outside of the flower—remains as a little spike. Through the centre of the two pairs, and having a long and a short stamen on either side, the long style runs curving so as to fit under the lip. Its lower end is set between four nutlets. Honey lies

The Self-Heal

at the bottom of the tube, and is protected by a thick hedge of hairs placed just above it.

The Self-heal, like the rest of its family, looks to the bees to fertilise it, its over-arching lip and petal tube being just made to fit their heads and probosces. It takes a bee about two seconds to extract the honey from a flower, and but a minute or so to pass through all the flowers in a head and effect their pollination. Its method is to dive into a flower; the stamen's side spikes keep the anthers in position. It pushes against them, the pollen falls on to its head as it sucks up the honey; it backs out of the blossom and transfers the pollen from its head and eyes first to its middle legs and then to its baskets on the hind ones, and in a flash is diving into the next flower to repeat the same operation, and, incidentally, to smear some of the pollen on to the curving style that runs up through the stamen pairs.

After fertilisation the corolla falls out of the sheath-like calyx and carries the stamens with it.

The calyx, however, remains in place, and so do the two bracts that support each tier. It is when all the purple, projecting corollas have fallen, and only the neat rings of the persistent calyces are left, that the aforementioned resemblance to an ear of corn is so marked.

The fruit is four little nuts that lie protected until they are ripe by the continually reddening calyx. The plant, however, does not trust its destiny wholly to them, though it indulges in a particularly long flowering season—namely, all through the summer months—for its creeping stems can throw up roots at any joint and thus propagate the plant. It is from these creeping stems that the flowering spikes rise, standing upright among the herbage three inches to a foot in height.

Sometimes there are found smaller and imperfect flowers—flowers that are only female and have either no stamens or merely rudimentary ones. One observer in Belgium reports that he has also found cleistogamous flowers upon it, i.e. flowers

The Self-Heal

which never open to admit visitors, but, within minute and poor corollas, fertilise their own ovules with their own pollen.

The leaves of this plant are not specially remarkable. They occur on short stalks in pairs down the stem. Roughish on top, their midrib at the back often carries hairs; the margins, too, are fringed with minute hairs.

The Self-heal is one of those hardy immigrants that have found their way to North America and tended to oust the native plants. It is there known as " Heart of the Earth," as well as by the pretty and not inappropriate name of " Blue Curls."

THE TEASEL

DIPSACUS SYLVESTRIS

ABOVE the vegetation at the dykeside curious egg-shaped heads were held aloft on tall stalks. Some of the heads were almost round,

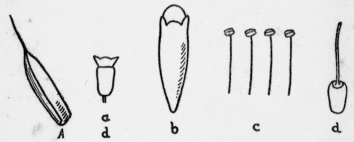

A, bract. *a d*, sepals on ovary. *b*, petals. *c*, stamens.
d, stigma, style, ovary.

these were greenest; some, rather more elongated, were ringed round the middle with a purple band; others, so elongated as to be almost cone-like, were purple from tip to base. All were a mass of semi-stiff spines, spines longest at the top of the head,

The Teasel

and each was enclosed, as it were, in a cage by
curving, narrow, green bracts set with small prickles,
which bracts arose in a ring at the base and, following
the line of the head, though a little outside it, curved
inwards at the tip. The tall stalks, ridged and
furrowed throughout their length, looked in the
bright sunlight as though studded with translucent
jewels, for over their whole surface colourless, sharp-
pointed prickles caught and reflected the sun's rays.
For some distance below the heads the stems were
bare—but for those multitudinous prickles—so that
the egg-shaped heads in their cages stood out in
splendid isolation ; then small pairs of leaves
appeared, joined directly by their bases to the main
stalk, and chiefly remarkable for a shining white
midrib which, at the back of the leaf, showed as a
thick outstanding rib, on which rib the ubiquitous
prickles were again in evidence. But in the lower
and larger pairs of leaves a new feature came in,
for there the bases joined round the stem and formed
basins which were partly filled with liquid, and in

which were the carcases of many little insects who had unwarily found a watery grave therein.

Thus, then, did the whole plant stand before us in simple dignity, distinguished, nay, unique, in appearance in this country, if we except its pale, insignificant replica, the Small Teasel, the only other species known here. Indeed, beside our three native species of scabious, there are no other members of its family—the *Dipsaceæ*—indigenous to our country.

Now there are many interesting points about a Teasel, and the first is the meaning of those leafy basins which surround the stalks. No doubt they are primarily intended to serve as a protection against large beasties, such as caterpillars and snails, as well as being traps for small creeping insects, and it is often suggested that this liquid, which contains a good deal of animal matter, is a sort of soup that may in some sort nourish the plant. In proof of this, it is urged that the basins are lined by some five thousand glandular hairs, which hairs are supposed to be for the purpose of absorbing this "soup." But a German investigator has recently thrown new light upon this matter. He points out that really the water is quite fresh in the basins, *and keeps so*, hence there is no nitrogenous food supplied by it to the plant. In fact, he notes that these very glandular hairs actually exude slime which coats the insect carcases and other matter that fall into the water. Another suggestion has probably something in it. It is that since the Teasel is a lover of moisture and prefers the saturated soil of marshy land, these cups of water up the stem tend to keep the plant always moist, and serve as reservoirs against a possible summer drought.

Even if the glandular hairs do not seem actually to absorb it appreciably, it is difficult not to believe that it keeps the tissues moist to some extent. Our forefathers used to collect this liquor and use it as a cosmetic and an eye-salve ; they also named the plant " Venus's Bath," " Venus's Cup," and " Our Lady's Basin."

Let us now pass to a closer examination of the

flower heads, choosing for inspection one of those
ringed with a broad purple band. The first thing
to notice is that each head is divided into an infinite
number of four-sided tubes—is pigeon-holed, so to
speak—which tubes are formed by boat-shaped
bracts set closely side by side, the prow of each
being produced into a dark-coloured spine. In the
Common Teasel this spine is straight, in the variety
known as the Fuller's Teasel it is hooked. So
regularly are these bracts placed that a double
spiral, one in each diagonal, is formed. The con-
tinuation of the stalk forms a thick axis to each
head. Above and below the purple band each
pigeon-hole is filled with a bud, which lies hidden in
its recesses, but in the purple band the buds have
developed into full-blown flowers whose purple
petals project somewhat beyond the green bracts.
It is a curious point worth notice that in the Teasel
the earliest line of development is a ring about
one-third of the way down, and from thence it
spreads upwards and downwards simultaneously.

The Teasel

Arguing from the daisy and similar floral heads, one would have expected it would have begun at the base and worked upwards, but probably that ring of florets develops first which gets the greatest amount of sunshine, and the shape of the head results in the development starting at this point.

If we isolate a boat-shaped bract and the flower it so carefully protects, we find that each floret consists of a long, tubular corolla made up of four petals marked by four lobes at the mouth, the lowest lobe being somewhat the largest. The upper, exposed part of the petals is a pale lilac colour; the lower, more hidden part, is white. Round the base of the corolla is a very small, green, cup-like calyx. On the first day of the flower's life four stamens protrude heads which are set across filaments standing on the corolla. Pollen is being shed from them. The ovary is below the corolla and a short style rises from it. Honey is produced by the upper part of the ovary and is collected in the petal tube. On the second day the stamens wither and the style grows and takes their place in protruding; the stigma has only one of its branches developed, the other is rudimentary, as it would otherwise get into the way of the bees and hover flies that frequent the heads. Insects that visit these flowers cannot walk over them promiscuously because of the stiff spines, so they must dive head-foremost into the tubes if they would partake of the honey. In their succession of dives to flowers of different ages they carry pollen from the younger to the older, and thus bring about fertilisation.

As the life of each flower ends, the corolla falls out of its niche, carrying the attached stamens with it. Since those that developed earliest naturally fall first, the ring that showed purple first shows green and empty pigeon-holes earliest, and an ever-widening green band follows upon the purple band. A single seed lies hidden in the recesses of these pigeon-holes, and is mature in the late autumn —the flowers themselves did not come until summer was well on. The ripe seeds are either shaken out by gusts of wind, or jerked out when the head springs back after catching on to some four- or two-footed passer-by. As the plant is a biennial, the seeds of this autumn will be the mature flowering plants of the summer after next.

The thick flower-heads of the Teasel are favourite homes of a certain grub, and these little worms were, in olden days, used as a charm against ague, but this hoary fable, vigorous in Queen Elizabeth's day, was scorned by Gerard, " they are nothing else but most vaine and trifling toies, as myself have proved a little before the impression hereof, having a most grievous ague and of long continuance. Notwithstanding Physicke charmes, these worms hanged about my neck, spiders put into a Walnut shell, and divers such foolish toies that I was constrained to take by fantasticke peoples' procurement, notwithstanding, I say, my helpe came from God Himselfe, for these medicines and all other such things did me no good at all."

But one use of the Teasel, dating from long

before Gerard's time, still remains unchallenged even in the most scientific and up-to-date manufactories of to-day, and that is for wool " fleecing." A certain cultivated variety, the Fuller's Teasel (*Dipsacus fullonum*)—Gerard's "tame Teasell"—is used because, as already mentioned, the spines of its flower-heads are hooked and not straight. These heads are fixed on the rim of a wheel, or on a cylinder, which is made to revolve against the surface of the cloth to be " fleeced," thus raising the nap. No machine has yet been invented which can compete with Teasel-bracts in their combined rigidity and elasticity, and this particular Teasel is grown largely in the West of England, and also imported from France, Africa, and America to meet the demands of our manufacturers. One large firm alone will use twenty thousand Teasel-heads in a year. The word " Teasel " itself is from the Anglo-Saxon *taesan*, meaning " to tease cloth." " Brushes-and-Combs," " Barber's Brush," " Card Teasel," and " Card Thistle " are synonyms for the plant.

THE MONEYWORT

LYSIMACHIA NUMMULARIA

THE Moneywort has one of those personalities which, whether in the plant or the animal world, seems to evoke the affections of all with whom it comes into contact. For such individuals

a, sepal. *b*, corolla. *c*, stamen ring. *c'*, single stamen.
d, stigma, style, ovary.

pet names seem naturally to take the place of the ordinary names, and so the Moneywort, that is, the " Money Plant," is far more often known by the endearing epithets of " Creeping Jenny," " Wandering Jenny," " Running Jenny," or sometimes " Creeping Joan " and " Wandering Sailor," all of

Wild Flowers as They Grow

which suggest definite personification and, of course, allude to its rapid trailing over the ground. " Meadow Runagates " has the same reference, with the added implication of those damp pastures by stream sides in which it is most at home. Tabernamontanus, one of the German plant writers about 1588, named the plant *Hirunclinaria* after the swallows, because " as swallows doe usually fly close to the ground so this plant cleaveth close to the earth," but his happy suggestion was never seriously endorsed.

The earliest English Herbal, that of Turner, who was a little previous to Tabernamontanus, speaks of it quaintly as " Herbe 2 pence and Two penigrasse," and as " Herb Twopence " and as " Twopenny Grass " it is still known.   Here the allusion is to the leaves which are set two and two in neatest fashion on the trailing stems, like a school out for a walk, and, being rounded (though each has a short, sharp tip) and lying always in two rows, faces turned to the sky, look like rows of pence. " Moneywort " and " Strings of Sovereigns " are names with the

The Moneywort

same idea underlying them, but no doubt in these the glamour of the big, golden flowers has suggested an opulency not strictly inherent in the "two-penny" leaves. Its specific name *nummularia* is from the Latin *nummulus*—money.

Now the Moneywort is a Loosestrife and own sister to the tall, yellow loosestrifes that, like it, also love gardens, and begin to hold up golden cups to the Midsummer sun, and "keep the flag flying" till well on into the autumn. (The purple loosestrife —*Lythrum salicaria*—is no relative, despite the name.)

The flowers of the Moneywort individually are even handsomer than those of the common yellow loosestrife. They spring singly on slender stalks just where a leaf joins the stem, and are large indeed in comparison with the rest of the little plant. Their five sepals are quite a feature, for they are large, pale-green, and heart-shaped, and rather "frilly" round the base, where the heart lobes have not room to spread. No doubt this "frilliness" is protective against small, creeping insects which might be tempted to invade a flower only just off the ground and so specially accessible. The five petals look distinct because they are so deeply lobed, but they are really a golden cup at the base. The stamens, also five in number, stand up rigidly within, but if one peers down into their supporting filaments one discovers that they are there joined to form a low ring. Moreover, with a lens, one can see that these filaments are covered with tiny golden hairs, or knobs, which must roughen the surface for the delicate legs of little flies to negotiate, and hence, perchance, still further protect the pollen that lies in the arrowhead-shaped anthers on top. These anthers are set each on its filament just where the "arrow-head" forks, so that they tilt and sway at the slightest touch. Note, as a small matter but one of some interest, that the stamens face the corresponding petals and do not, as is usual in flowers, alternate with them. This is a peculiarity of the whole family—the Moneywort belongs to the

The Moneywort

Primulaceæ,—and it seems to imply that, at some time or another, a whole ring of outer stamens has been eliminated from the flower's structure.

The ovary within appears normal, and the style is long enough to bring the stigma just below the level of the stamens. Pollen from these stamens must often fall upon it, but it means no more to the ovules within the ovary than if a little dust fell on that receptive surface. The flower is absolutely sterile to its own pollen. On the other hand, pollen from other Moneywort flowers does not seem to have much effect, at any rate in this country, for, as a rule, when the flowers are done no fruit follows. It is rather inexplicable and it has been argued that the plant is, therefore, not a true native, and that there is something in our climate that does not suit it. But it is probably because it has found out a simpler, and more reliable method of propagating itself, and therefore does not trouble to set seed.

This alternative method of continuing existence

Wild Flowers as They Grow

lies in its trailing shoots—its "stolons." Now a "stolon" is defined as a creeping stem which dies off every year and is abundantly beset by leaves not very far apart. Close to the turned-up tip of each stolon, in the angle formed by little leaf-stalks, buds appear which produce roots. These roots pass into the ground and establish themselves. Then when winter comes the stem and leaves die down between the old root and the new one, but when the following spring arrives a new plant arises where the little roots entered the earth. Hence from a single plant which sends out a stolon in various directions many new plants may appear by this so-called "vegetative" method of reproduction. The stems of the Moneywort are quadrangular, and leaves and stems are all quite smooth.

A little, unexpected romance has been discovered in the life-history of the Moneywort. It appears that it is at times the host of a minute, single-celled, green plant—an alga—whose name, *Phyllobium dimorphum*, is really more imposing than

The Moneywort

the plant itself. *Phyllobium* also frequents damp woods and flooded meadows, and at one stage of its life it is just a single cell swimming about in drops of water by means of two oars or " flagella." When it meets a Moneywort leaf it sends out delicate tubes which pass into the tissues through the little mouths, or stomata, that exist for the water evaporation of the leaf, and there it spreads. Later the protoplasm of these tubes collects into one large cell, which rests throughout the winter, and in the spring breaks up into a number of little bodies, which pass out into the surrounding moisture. These bodies meet in pairs and unite their substance, and then put out the two oars and, swimming, begin life afresh. Sometimes, instead of forming one large cell, a number of small resting cells take its place, hence the second name " *dimorphum* "—of two forms. It does not appear that this uninvited guest wants anything from the Moneywort but a home—the shelter of its tissues—to develop in. This is proved by the fact that it as often enters dead leaves as

Wild Flowers as They Grow

living ones, and is quite unaffected if the leaf dies during the time it is honouring it with its presence. Single-celled plants which live thus within the tissues of other and higher plants without benefiting their host, and taking nothing but shelter from them, are known as the *Endosphæraceæ*.

A word as to the reputed virtues of the Moneywort in olden days. It was one of the many "best possible" woundworts. "In a word, there is not a better wound-herb, no not tobacco itselfe, nor any other what-soever," said an old herbalist. And so it was called "Centum morbia," while again it was a specific for whooping cough, "being boyled with Wine and Honey . . . it prevaileth against that violent cough in children commonly called the chinne-cough, but it should be chine-cough, for it doth make as it were the very chine-bone to shake." Finally, most curious of all, we are gravely told that if serpents hurt or wounded themselves, they turned to this plant for healing and, so it was sometimes called "Serpentaria."

THE SUCCORY

CICHORIUM INTYBUS

STIFF, straight stems, rough and ribbed, bordered the road which lay like a curving, white ribbon under the late summer sun, and each stem was decked with sundry blue-rayed stars set

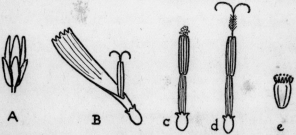

A, involucre of bracts. B, a floret showing petal ray, stamen head, forked stigma, ovary. *c*, pollen mass, stamens, ovary. *d*, the same with stigma protruding. *e*, fruit.

close upon it, stars which somewhat reminded one of the dandelions lying on the ground around, only they were fewer-rayed and of a glorious blue instead of a crude yellow. The brilliant blue showed up in

Wild Flowers as They Grow

special contrast to the white of the chalk that gleamed from between the herbage and from the bare road, and this star-studding turned the ugly stems into quite fairy wands. No wonder " The Professor at the Breakfast Table " found "the tall-stemmed Succory, setting its pale blue flowers aflame, one after the other, sparingly as the lights are kindled in the candelabra of decaying palaces where the heirs of dethroned monarchs are dying out," a plant that is " a ray of the Divine beauty." A chalky soil and the dry roadside form its favourite environment :—

> " Oh, not in ladies' gardens
>   My peasant posy,
> Smile thy dear blue eyes,
> Nor only—nearer to the skies
> In upland pastures, dim and sweet,
>   But by the dusty road
>   Where tired feet
>   Toil to and fro,
>   Where flaunting Sin
>   May see thy heavenly hue
> Or weary Sorrow look from thee
>   Towards a heavenly blue ! "

(Margaret Deland.)

The Succory

All up the stem at intervals are placed the blue blooms—not flowers, *pace* the Professor—for each is a composite head of a number of florets, quite stalkless and in pairs (though just occasionally there are three together). Those still in the bud stage are long, narrow, blunt-pointed, enclosed in six or eight enfolding green bracts which have a row of minute, erect hairs running down their backs, the hairs being tipped with glands. Below each pair of blooms is a leaf, stalkless, clasping the stem and narrow, long and pointed. Lower down the leaves are larger and coarser and cut into side lobes, in addition to the main, terminal lobe; this intersecting allows the light to pass between to the hairy leaves that, at the base, spread right on the ground.

The blooms that are open—and they open between six and seven every morning—can be seen to have two tiers of protecting bracts all with rows of glandular hairs, the outermost and shorter turned-back ones having also a fringe of these hairs. The bloom itself certainly looks far more like an ordinary

Wild Flowers as They Grow

single flower than a flower-colony, for it is composed of a ring of blue rays corresponding to ordinary petals with a centre of stamen-like objects. But if one looks carefully one finds that to every petal there is a corresponding erect column, and the two together form a complete flower. Therefore each blue ray, instead of being a single petal, is really five petals joined together into a five-notched strap, which curls round near its base to form a tube.

If one of these florets be carefully drawn entire out of the bloom it will be found to have, at the very bottom, a tiny, cream-coloured ovary rather flattened from side to side. At the top of this, instead of the ring of hairs, so usual in the members of the *Compositæ* family, there is a ring of minute scales to represent the calyx. Then comes the little white petal tube fringed with hairs and expanding into the long, blue ray. Peering into the tube shows one that there are five white filaments running down to the ovary and supporting a long, greenish-blue column—their united five anthers. If one examines

The Succory

a bloom in the early morning one sees that this column is surmounted by a pile of white grains. As the day passes one finds that this pile was formed by a piston pushing up through the hollow anther-tube and pressing out its contents—as if a sweep pushed the soot *up* through the top of the chimney instead of bringing it down. The piston rod—the style—goes on growing and pushing and, ultimately gets right through the pile. White pollen grains adhere to it, and soon above the anther column stands another column, white, because thickly coated with shining grains. Finally, this piston column opens into two branches which stand curling outwards right above the grains, but not a single grain has so far touched the surface of the fork, thick as they are on the column beneath it.

Now the Succory is a typical humble-bee flower, its colouring—" Succory to match the sky," said Emerson—specially appealing to the Bombus bees, and when they come no doubt they will bring pollen from other blooms, or maybe only from adjacent florets, and this will be deposited on the fork. But in any case in the early afternoon the bloom closes, its petal-rays draw together, the central columns are all pressed one against another, and those curling forks necessarily touch the pollen-coated styles of their neighbours and thus fertilisation happens. Linnæus used the Chicory as one of the flowers in his Floral Clock at Upsala because of its regularity in opening at five a.m. and closing at ten a.m. in that latitude. The fruit of this plant consists of hard, dry little objects packed on to the flat stalk-end.

But the big tap root of the Succory is, after all, the part that is really familiar to everyone, though one does not recognise it in the dark brown grains that are mixed with one's coffee. It is thick and white and rather hard, and for commercial purposes it is sliced, kiln-dried and roasted, and then ground up. It has no aroma, and none of the alkaloid "caffeine," but it is often thought actually to improve the coffee that it adulterates. In Belgium it is used as a drink without any admix-

The Succory

ture of coffee. Enormous quantities of the plant are cultivated to provide the grocers with " chicory." Abroad, too, the young and tender roots are boiled and eaten with butter as a very palatable vegetable.

It is suggested that the name Succory came from the Latin *succurrere*, "to run under," because of the depth to which the root penetrates. Perhaps, however, it is only a corruption of " Chicory," or " Cichorium," a word of Egyptian origin, which in various forms is the name of the plant with practically every European nation. The Arabian physicians called it " Chicourey," and after the Conquest their influence and writings permeated everywhere.

But the plant makes yet another appeal on the edible side. The French winter salad, " Barbe de Capucin," consists of its blanched leaves. The seeds are sown in heat and kept in the dark, or else young plants sown in May are taken up in the autumn, their older leaves cut off, their roots shortened, and then planted in the dark. The young, on-coming leaves develop without green colour.

THE HEDGE STACHYS

STACHYS SYLVATICA

A DETESTABLE smell (especially when bruised), rough, nettle-like leaves, rough, square stalks, and a spike of dark purple-red flowers of no particular beauty is not a combination of

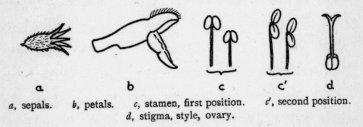

a, sepals.   *b*, petals.   *c*, stamen, first position.   *c′*, second position.
d, stigma, style, ovary.

qualities that makes an attractive personality. But, at any rate, the Hedge Stachys does not know that crowning disgrace of to-day—unobtrusive mediocrity, to be one of the undistinguished rank and file—its smell alone raises it above that, and gives it a forceful and definite, if unpleasing, personality. Among

The Hedge Stachys

those many other rough, nettle-like herbs that choke the hedgeside and perplex the non-botanist with their close resemblances it, at least, stands out, for the mere handling of the plant reveals it infallibly, and even after it is thrown away in disgust the evil aroma clings to one's fingers and keeps its memory green.

There are five species of Stachys growing wild in our country—the once much-valued Betony ; the Woundwort, a doubtful native and actually known as the *Stachys Germanica ;* the Marsh Stachys, whose smell is bad but not *so* bad ; the low-creeping Field Stachys ; and our friend of the illustration—and all are more or less coarse and hairy herbs. The Hedge Stachys has thick, creeping roots that throw up tall stems, two, three, or, maybe, four feet high. The stalked leaves are arranged up them in pairs, each leaf being on the opposite side of the square stem to its partner. The pair of leaves above and the pair below arise from the other two sides of the square, and thus not only are the leaves opposite to one another, the pairs are also at right angles to each other. This alternation of position of the pairs prevents, of course, undue overshadowing of one pair by that immediately above it. It has been shown that it is a mechanical advantage for the supporting stem to be square when the leaves are placed in opposite pairs. The leaves themselves are heart-shaped, with a bold, saw-like margin, and they feel like velvet to the touch, so dense are the hairs upon them. Their disagreeable juices cause cows and horses to give them a wide berth, but it is said that sheep and goats will nibble at them if herbage is scanty. Country folk sometimes aver that toads prefer the shelter of these plants to others less odorous, but most probably this theory rests on the mere idle supposition that one disagreeable thing must needs prefer the company of other disagreeable things.

The flower-spike tops the stem. The flowers are arranged in rings—" whorls "—always six in each ring, and the rings are set one above another up the spike, say half an inch or more apart. Close under each ring is a pair of small, sharp, pointed green bracts, otherwise the stalk between is bare. The buds and youngest flowers are in the top stories, then come tiers with the flowers in full bloom ; below these are rings of merely empty calyx tubes, their five sharp points very much in evidence, for the red-purple corollas have withered and fallen away. At the bottom of every empty calyx tube four nutlets can now be seen to be lying; in the upper tiers they are white or tinged with brown, in the lowermost they are shining black. Here and there a gap in the fours is showing where some nutlet has been shot out as the calyx dried and con-tracted.

Turn back to the tiers where the flowers are still blooming in full force. Out of the five-pointed calyx cup the long tube of the red-purple corolla projects. It is about two-fifths of an inch long, and since it is often half-filled with honey it is obvious that the Hedge Stachys—like many other

Wild Flowers as They Grow

unattractive individuals—possesses a considerable amount of hidden sweetness. The corolla tube ends in two sinister jagged lips; the upper lip— the smaller—stands upright slightly overarching, the upper side of the arch being covered with white hairs. The lower lip is long, narrow, and three-lobed. Round the mouth of the tube are numerous hairs and a curious streaking and white marbling of the ruddy petals. The shape of the mouth is a rounded arch with a deep trench, or channel, in its floor; the white hairs are particularly stiff and prominent on the side walls of this deep trench, and serve to keep insect visitors to the centre of the channel.

The Stachys, like the dead nettle, with whose structure, indeed, it is almost identical, lays itself out for Bombus bees, hive bees, and, as one would expect from its smell and colour, for flies, though it is necessary that these should be of the long-tongued kind. No others could reach the honey. The stamens are four, in two pairs, lying close under the

The Hedge Stachys

roof of the upper arching lip, with cream anthers on red filaments, the filaments carrying quite a brush of hairs half-way up. In the centre of them, also under the upper lip, runs the red, ovary column with a very pronounced fork at its tip.

Now, if a bud be opened and its secrets laid bare before it is time to unclose its lips and expose its mouth, it will be found that the fork of the style is already fully open. The style is longer than the stamen filaments, so this stigma fork is above the anthers. One pair of anthers, cream and closed, lie just beneath it on but slightly curved filaments, but the second pair of anthers are much lower in the buds, their filaments curling right over. At first the two anthers of each stamen are smooth, closed bags side by side, then they move apart at an angle and begin to split on the side facing the mouth, and then, still before the bud opens, they turn so as to be in line one above the other, the slits widen and cream pollen grains begin to appear out of them. At this stage the bud opens its mouth.

Wild Flowers as They Grow

The stigma fork is the most prominent part of the flower. Just below and behind it lies a mass of pollen issuing from the eight anther cells, and the tube glistens with the promise of honey. Any bee or long-tongued fly approaching settles on the lower lip and creeps carefully up the centre of its channelled floor into the dim, red-glowing tunnel of the petal tube. The forked stigma touches it first, sweeping along its head and back as it moves in, and thus collecting pollen for itself if any be there. As the insect passes beyond the stigma it plunges right into the pollen mass behind and receives a thorough dusting, which dusting of pollen keeps fairly in the centre of the bee's back, because all the anthers lie centrally in two long lines, four in each, and this pollen dust falls exactly along the line which will be swept by the projecting stigma of the next flower visited. Apparently every flower gets fertilised ; in a spike of thirteen tiers, six flowers in each, one will get three hundred and twelve black seeds. The mechanism of the flower is interesting, especially if

The Hedge Stachys

one trace it with a lens from the early bud stage to the withering flower.

It is said that a yellow dye can be obtained from the plant, and it has been suggested that the very tough fibres of its stem might be utilised commercially; it has also been classed among the woundworts as good for stanching blood, but in none of these particulars does it seem to have special value; it is therefore difficult to understand why, a century ago, the "Universal Herball" should think it worth while to give minute directions for its propagation and cultivation as if it were a plant of moment to our great-grandfathers.

THE YARROW OR MILFOIL

ACHILLEA MILLEFOLIA

"THE Yarrow and the Sneezewort," says
Maeterlinck, "march along the roads
like silent schoolgirls clad in a dull uniform . . .
wearing the practical grey livery of autumn which

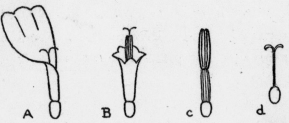

A, ray floret.   B, central floret.   *c*, stamen, ovary,   *d*, stigma, style, ovary.

already is felt to be at hand." Under the brilliant
sun of the passing July days when the grey-green
stems first begin to assert themselves, this greyness
is accentuated by the tight clusters of dull-grey
buds that tip the branches. Nowhere is there a

184

YARROW OR MILFOIL

The Yarrow or Milfoil

hint of that joyous vividness that is so marked a characteristic of the plants of the spring, for over the whole of the Yarrow Nature has thrown a filmy veiling of grey silken hairs. The plant is, indeed, at this stage the apotheosis of the unobtrusive, and, even later, when the flowers come, detail is lost in their insignificance and matters are not much better. Moreover, the magnificent constitution of the plant enables it to flourish by the dustiest road-side and in the most neglected of spots, and so familiar association with dust and dullness is added to its other drawbacks, and it has become the symbol of the commonplace—a thing without power to charm. But make the Yarrow rare and magnify it fourfold, and it would be at once acclaimed for its beauty! While as for its inherent virtues our forefathers would be astonished at our apathy on this point. Let us, then, give the plant our sympathetic consideration.

Now even in the early, greyest days of its career a flower-lover will note the rigid, elegantly-

Wild Flowers as They Grow

grooved column of its main stem, and the miniature reproduction of it in the branches ; also the fern-like leaves of many leaflets, folded face to face, leaflet to leaflet in the young leaves, but stretching apart in older leaves and showing that each leaflet as well as each leaf is daintily cut in a filmy fashion. Therefore do the country folk call it " Milfoil " or " Thousand Leaf," Latin, *Mille folia*. The main rib of the whole leaf is a white channel bordered with dark green, and the upward tilt of the leaf ensures that all rain and dew that it collects shall run along this channel and from it trickle down the furrowed main stem to the root. Pungent juices lie within the grey-green tissues, to which juices the old herbalists attributed many virtues. " Most men say that the leaves chewed, and especially green, are a remedy for the toothache," says one, and it is quite possible that the toothache might then be the lesser evil and forgotten in the noxiousness of the remedy. " The leaves being put into the nose do cause it to bleed and ease the paine of the megrim,"

The Yarrow or Milfoil

is another prescription which gave the plant its old English name of " Nose-Bleed," " Old Man's Pepper " and " Sneezewort," though this last name is perhaps more properly applied to the other species of Yarrow native here, namely, the *Achillea ptarmica*. Even to-day country people still stuff the leaves up their nose when they suffer from headaches due to congestion in the head.

A few days later than when our first observations were made some of the grey, massed buds become topped with a suggestion of white. The whole cluster is greener, too, having shed most of the covering white hairs. Each bud now appears wrapped in silvery scales with broad midrib and brown edges. Still a day or two later and little white rolls of petals, five as a rule, can be detected in each bud. Then suddenly, all together, the petals complete their uncurling and spread, and the united action of the buds places before us a flat, white, floral disk, apparently composed of many flowers, each with a golden centre. But a great surprise is in store for us, for

Wild Flowers as They Grow

on closer inspection we find we have really cluster within cluster, for each of the little apparent flowers, so small that a shilling would cover twenty of them, proves to be itself a head of flowers. The five or six short, broad rays, shaped like palm-leaf fans, are not merely petals, but flowers consisting of five united petals—the fan part—and a minute tube, the handle—which tube encloses a still more minute ovary with a forked style. The yellow centre, which we took for merely stamens, is really made up of several white, tubular corollas, whose mouths are filled with brilliant yellow stamen-heads, five heads all joined together going to each. But the united stamen-heads are so prominent that the surrounding corolla is practically negligible at a cursory glance. In the older of these inner florets a rod from the ovary below thrusts itself through the stamens pushing out their pollen—the anthers retracting a little—and then opens into a fork. Notice there are no stamens in the outer, more showy florets. Under a lens it can be seen that the stigma forks

The Yarrow or Milfoil

are covered with pollen dust, not from the stamens in their respective florets, for these are below them, but from the stamens of adjacent florets and clusters. For if the Yarrow is no favourite with man it is immensely popular with little flies of many sorts ; in fact, about one hundred and twenty different kinds of insects have been seen visiting the flat clusters—and fine platforms these make, too, for their peregrinations and fine feeding grounds, also, so far as pollen is concerned, and pollen is often quite as acceptable as honey. Each floret will eventually produce a single, little, dry seed of no special interest. The plant does not, however, trust to its seeds solely for its propagation. It probably owes its prevalence far more to its strong, creeping root that forcibly pushes its way about, however stony or hard the soil around.

Sometimes the Yarrow flower-heads are attacked by gall-mites, and then most extraordinary things happen, " the flowers being metamorphosed into green funnels with jagged mouths, and into small

Wild Flowers as They Grow

flat-lobed and toothed foliage leaves, whilst short, green, scale-like leaflets rise from the midribs of these leaves representing the metamorphosed stamens," says Kerner.

To the country girl the chief interest of the Yarrow lies in the fact that it is a first-rate fortune-teller. One has only to stitch up an ounce of Yarrow in a piece of flannel and put it under one's pillow, and say before getting into bed :

> " Thou pretty herb of Venus tree,
>   Thy true name it is Yarrow,
>   Now who my bosom friend must be,
>   Pray tell thou me to-morrow,"

for one's dreams to declare infallibly who is to be one's true love ! Sometimes the ritual is a little different. A maiden will rise exactly at the first hour of dawn and gather three sprigs of the plant, saying as she does so :

> " Good morning, good morning, good Yarrow,
>   And thrice good morning to thee ;
>   Tell me before this time to-morrow
>   Who my true love is to be,"

The Yarrow or Milfoil

and then place them in her shoe or her glove and go forth in full faith that she will meet her future husband during the day.

Certain of the remedial virtues that are supposed to lie in its leaves have already been mentioned, but there still remains to tell of the wonderful ointment that can be made from it, an ointment that will quickly heal up all wounds. The Icelander and the Highlander specially used it and do perhaps to this day, following a tradition from the mythological days of Achilles, who learnt the secret from the Centaur, Chiron, that he might heal his soldiers wounded at the siege of Troy. Therefore is the plant still *Achillea* to the botanist, and " Woundwort," " Soldier's Woundwort," " Knighten Milfoil," or " Kinglatin Milfoil " to the children of to-day, even though they have never heard of the heroic days of Helen of Troy. At one time, too, this ointment was further esteemed for its power to stay the shedding of the hair. Milfoil tea has a fame that still lives in certain remote parts, where it is

Wild Flowers as They Grow

brewed by the old wives for sufferers from the ague. The women of the Orkneys give it to those who are subject to fits of melancholy.

As to the name Yarrow, it is somewhat of a mystery how the plant got it. Apparently it has annexed one of the vervain's names, namely, the Greek *hiera botane*, i.e. holy herb, and since the Greek *hi* becomes *g* or *y* in our language, the " *hiera* " has become " Yarrow "—at least, this is Dr. Prior's surmise, which must be accepted for want of a better. In Wales the plant is called the " Death Flower," since it is considered to presage death if brought into the house. Probably the superstition arose because the Yarrow is a plant that frequents the churchyard. For this reason, too, it is used as a funeral token.

THE LING OR HEATHER

CALLUNA VULGARIS

" An empty sky, a world of heather ;
Purple of foxglove, yellow of broom,
We two among them, wading together,
Shaking out honey, treading perfume."

(Jean Ingelow.)

IN that " world of heather " three kinds of
Heath are found in company ; first, here and

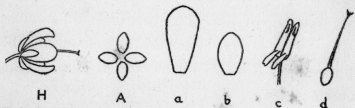

H, flower, showing style projecting.   A, bracts.   *a*, sepal.   *b*, petal.
   c, stamen opening by pores. *d*, stigma, style, ovary.

there, in patches, is the Cross-leaved Heath (*see*
Vol. III.) with its delicate, shell-pink flowers clustered all together at the top of its stalks ; then,

Wild Flowers as They Grow

more plentiful, is the Bell or Scotch Heath, whose
red-purple spikes form masses of ruddy hue that
satisfy the most colour-loving eye, showier far than
the first-named, not because the individual flowers
are any larger, but because they are of deeper hue
and are thickly set up a long spike instead of being
a few together in a cluster; thirdly, there is the
Common Ling, or Heather, of our picture, which,
though the least beautiful, is the dominant member
of this plant society—the background of that
Heather world on which the foxglove, the gorse and
the Heaths paint splashes of colour and amid which,
too, the bilberry struggles to maintain a foothold.
And all this little community are honey-producing
and fragrant, and together form—

"Those wastes of heath
Stretching for miles to lure the bee,"

that we call "the moors." Curiously enough, though
Heather honey—reddish and Heather flavoured—is
to-day ranked the most excellent among honeys by
connoisseurs, Gerard was not of this opinion—"of

HEATH OR LING

The Ling or Heather

these floures the Bees do gather bad honey," he
says, and there is no doubt that appreciation of
it is somewhat an acquired taste. It was largely
to this honey that Heather Beer owed its reputed
marvellous flavour—reputed only, for the brewing
of this cherished drink of legendary Picts is one of
the lost arts of mankind, though occasionally in
some outlandish Highland spot shallow receptacles
are found which, tradition says, are the ancient
brewing vats.

The Ling is a remarkable plant, most tenacious
of life and hardy to a degree, accommodating in its
likes and dislikes, thriving upon soil of all sorts,
cheerfully facing much sterility, and only daunted by
extreme dryness. Its tough, fibrous roots live twenty
or thirty years, and throw up year by year fresh
branches—wiry stems which carry tiny branchlets,
which branchlets are clothed with a coat of minute
leaves arranged in four neat rows and overlapping
like tiles on a roof. But minute as are these leaves
—they run thirty or so to the half-inch—they are

distinctly interesting, and their structure is not at first sight obvious. Each is stalkless and of plain outline, but is rolled backwards in such a way that its edges almost meet behind, and thus the under-surface is the lining of a tunnel. It is into this tunnel that all the water pores open. Just where the leaf meets the stem it is produced back into two little tails. The structure of the leaf cannot be made out by the unaided eye—it needs a lens to show the line of the slit at the back. The object of the close pressing to the stem and the curling back is to minimise the giving off of water by the plant, and to enable it to withstand drought as much as possible. It will be found that in the Bell Heath the leaves are not so much curled or so crowded, while in the Cross-leaved Heath there is still less curling and crowding. Perhaps these three stages of adaptation to withstand drought are the measure of the relative prevalence of the plants on the moor.

The leaves are evergreen and leathery, and, on

The Ling or Heather

account of the tannin juices they contain, are not tempting to browsing animals.

The flowers as well as the leaves are very small. They are specially noticeable in their sepals and in their stamens. The four minute green bracts at the base of the flower are not the sepals, though they look as though they were, for the four sepals are large, considerably larger than the petals, and, indeed, quite enclosing them, and, like them, are pink and of a parchment-like texture which does not wither, hence the flowers remain pink and fresh-looking for months. The stamens are twice as many as the sepals, and each anther has two little tails, or horns, covered with hairs, stretching out from its outer side. These eight anthers are arranged in a close ring round the style inside the sepals, their sixteen horns forming a complete and barricading circle. The style is very long, and projects far from the flower. The ovary is at the bottom of the flower, and a ring-like nectary is round its base.

Now the flowers of the Ling do not hang like the

flowers of its companion Heaths do, they are horizontal or even slightly tilted upwards. When a bee comes clambering over the spikes it therefore thrusts its proboscis under the projecting style (which it must smear with any pollen that is on its body), and so strikes against the stamen horns barricade. The anthers open by two pores, but since the anthers touch one another at these very points the pollen cannot fall out until the bee jars them apart as it strikes the barricade of the sixteen horns. But then out falls the pollen in a shower right on to the bee. And so it goes off laden to strike the outstretching stigma of the next flower visited. The ovary is four-chambered, with a number of seeds, and it develops into a capsule. Though it ripens that autumn it does not usually open till the following spring, when it slits in four places, and the light little seeds are dispersed by the wind. But it is probable the wind plays yet another part in the life-story of the Ling. Though it is so very attractive to bees and flies, the plant

The Ling or Heather

apparently does not rely on them entirely ; its pollen is very light and powdery, and as that not carried off by the bees lies loose in the horizontal flowers— it cannot fall out as it does in a bell-flower—it is blown out in clouds by the wind, and must necessarily powder all those projecting stigmas around it.

Though Heather is usually pink, white, or more or less pale, Heather is sometimes found, and everyone knows that the finding thereof is an omen of happiness and good fortune.

As for the synonyms of this plant, besides Heather and Ling it is also known as " Grig," " Griglands," " Gowlins," " Dog Heath," " Small Heath," and " Basam." The Ling, once included among the Heaths—the *Ericas*, now forms a distinct genus, *Calluna*, all to itself in the family *Ericaceæ*.

But there is still another most interesting point about the Ling. It is one of those plants that lives with a partner, to the mutual advantage of both, for on its roots it carries a fungus, and this fungus can absorb food from the peaty soil in a way the

Wild Flowers as They Grow

plant could not do unaided. The fungus works this up and passes it on in suitable form to the plant, and in return it draws upon the living sap of its host. This mutual advantage partnership is known as symbiosis.

The periodic firing of moors by gamekeepers is for the purpose of keeping the Ling dominant, as it is specially desirable for the grouse. The firing destroys all the vegetation in the quarter fired, but only for the time being, for Ling seedlings immediately spring up, and soon the plant again is reigning.

1555

PRINTED BY CASSELL & COMPANY, LIMITED, LA BELLE SAUVAGE, LONDON, E.C.